GW00567323

Practical Activities, Investigations and Games

Mathematics Key Stage 3

Fran Ashworth

SOUTHGATE

Copyright © Dorset County Council 1992
Copyright © Illustrations Southgate Publishers Ltd

First published 1992 by Southgate Publishers

Southgate Publishers Ltd
Glebe House, Church Street, Crediton, Devon EX17 2AF

All rights reserved. No part of this publication may be reproduced, copied or transmitted in any form or by any means, electronic, mechanical, photocopying, recording or otherwise, without the prior written permission of the publisher or in accordance with the Copyright, Design and Patents Act 1988.

Parts of this book may be photocopied by the purchaser or the purchaser's school/organisation for use within that school/organisation only.

Printed and bound in Great Britain by Short Run Press Ltd, Exeter.

British Library Cataloguing in Publication Data.
A CIP catalogue record for this book is available from the British Library.

ISBN 1 85741 020 3

CONTENTS

INTRODUCTION

This book began several years ago as an attempt to match the syllabus I was supposed to cover with the investigative activities I was trying to use in my classroom. Now that we have a National Curriculum for Mathematics I have rewritten it to match the Attainment Targets.

The book is for teachers. I have often been asked to hand out materials which can be given straight to the pupils. I cannot do this for a class I have not met or worked with. Every group of pupils is different and the style and level of presentation will need to take this into account. The beauty of investigative work and of games is their flexibility. Whenever I make up a game, I make up easier and harder versions of it for particular groups of pupils. Everyone in the class can thereby be 'doing the same thing' but at a level where they can cope. Many investigations can be varied slightly so that each group in a class is given a suitable challenge and the quicker pupils do not have to start with the very simplest case. There are photocopiable pupil pages in this book but they are only suggestions. I hope that teachers will take the ideas, try them out and adjust them to their own needs.

It is impossible with activities like these to predict which levels the pupils will achieve. For this reason I make no suggestions as to which should be tried with younger pupils and which with older. In fact there is no reason why an activity cannot be repeated after a couple of years when the pupils have more mathematical experience, to see where else or how much further it could have gone.

The New Attainment Targets (NATs) are listed at the head of each activity. These Attainment Targets are set out in the Consultative Document issued in May 1991. They are as follows:

NAT 1   Using and Applying Mathematics (formerly ATs 1 and 9)
NAT 2   Number (formerly ATs 2, 3, 4, and part of 8)
NAT 3   Algebra (formerly ATs 5, 6 and 7)
NAT 4   Shape and Space (formerly ATs 10, 11, and part of 8)
NAT 5   Data Handling (formerly ATs 12, 13 and 14)

By condensing fourteen Targets into five without losing any content, the working party has had to put a lot more into each level, each Statement of Attainment having several sub-statements in the Programme of Study. No activity in this book is likely therefore to cover a whole level of any Target. Mention of a level means only that the activity is contributing to *some* statement(s) within that level.

An example of how the activities can be related to the Attainment Targets is given here. For the activity entitled Golf Balls parts of the following Targets are covered.

Pupils:

Select suitable equipment and materials	NAT 1
Explain what they are doing and why	NAT 1
Make changes and predict how they will work	NAT 1
Choose suitable units of measurement	NAT 2/3
Draw things to scale	NAT 2/5
Measure and draw angles	NAT 4/5
Decide on how accurate their measurements need to be	NAT 2/6
Work out areas	NAT 4/5, 7
Work out volumes	NAT 4/5, 7
Draw nets for solids	NAT 4
Find out if shapes will tessellate	NAT 4/6
Draw pictures of solids	NAT 4/6
Show results on charts or graphs	NAT 5

When the pupils test the strength of the box design they will be working from the *Science National Curriculum*.

Pupils:

Describe how they tested for strength	AT 10/5
Decide which design is the best by looking at what it is made of, how much it costs and how strong it is	AT 10/7

All planning and design will contribute to Statements of Attainment in the *Design and Technology National Curriculum*	NAT 1, 2, 3, 4

I do not expect these activities to cover everything. In fact I am not sure that all mathematics could, or should, be taught in this way. When it is, however, I find that the pupils become more involved, more motivated and remember more clearly and for longer what they found out.

I am aware that many of the activities will also contribute to Statements of Attainment in other subjects, but since this is essentially a mathematics book I leave the cross-curricular links to you.

A symbol is shown at the top of each activity. This denotes whether the activity is:

a practical activity   an investigation   a game

Fran Ashworth
*Mathematics Advisory Team Leader,
Dorset*

TACKLING INVESTIGATIONS

This should give you a piece of work which you can show to other people.
You may also find it useful for yourself. You can look back at it if you
come across a similar problem later on.

Alien Bricks

EQUIPMENT

Isometric paper

Multilink cubes

Cardboard box as the energy converter (not essential but amusing if you put buttons on labelled ON / OFF / NOT SURE / SELF DESTRUCT / HEAVY LOAD / etc. also "MADE ON ALPHA CENTAURI by GALAXY Ltd." etc.)

Worksheet 1 (page 78)

INSTRUCTIONS

'Friendly aliens landed in the field behind my house last week whilst I was mowing the lawn. I was a bit surprised because although all sorts of strange things (hot air balloons, microlights) have landed there in the past I'd never before seen a space ship. Two people who looked quite like my Uncle Edward, except they had green hair (my uncle is bald) and purple faces (Uncle's face only goes purple after five flights of stairs), got out and came over to me. We talked using a special translator box (we wouldn't have managed otherwise because when they spoke it sounded to me like water going down the plug-hole) and they asked me the way to New York.

I invited them inside for a cup of tea and a piece of fruit cake and showed them on my atlas where New York was. They stayed quite a while for a chat, (they also had a short conversation with my chickens) and before they left one of them nipped back to the ship to get me a present.

This is what they gave me: it's an 'Energy Converter' and when you put things inside it they grow bigger each day. They told me to put one of these bricks (aliens use cube shaped bricks!) into it and leave it. Each day it will grow bigger. Different coloured bricks grow in different ways so I have to watch the pattern of each one very carefully for a few days to see exactly how it grows.

Can you work out what is happening each time?'

VARIATIONS

'For each pattern find out:

How long to leave them in the energy converter if you need 100 bricks, 500 bricks, n bricks?

If you left them in for two weeks, a year, n days, how many bricks would you end up with?

Can you make up some growing patterns of your own?'

Ancient Counting

EQUIPMENT

Number squares cut or torn into ten pieces (page 8)

Squared paper

INSTRUCTIONS

Hand out sets of the cut or torn number squares to the class.

'An ancient parchment has been found in a jar at the bottom of your garden. Unfortunately, as the archaeologist tries to lift it out, it breaks into several pieces. She brings it indoors and asks you to help her piece it back together'.

When you have done this you realize it is a type of number square. You copy it on to squared paper because the archaeologist has to take the pieces to the museum. When she has gone you try to work out what it means.

For example what would ⌐iii⌐ •⚊ mean? How would you write a hundred in this counting system? What do each of the symbols represent in our counting system?'

VARIATIONS

'Make up a counting system of your own and give it to someone else to puzzle out. Ask them some questions about numbers which are higher than the ones on your square.'

ANCIENT COUNTING NUMBER SQUARES

Cut or tear along the thick lines.

The Answer is . . .

NAT 2	NAT 3	NAT 4	NAT 5
2 3 4 5 6 7 8	2 3	2 3 4 5	3 4

EQUIPMENT

Paper
Pencil
Calculator

INSTRUCTIONS

Choose any number. Tell the class the answer to a question is that number: what was the question? Encourage them to make up questions in a written (word) form as well as in maths notation, and to use all four rules. Later ask them to change their story-type ones into maths notation.

VARIATIONS

1. The question must have fractions in it.
2. Or decimals.
3. Or percentages.
4. Or ratios.
5. Or directed numbers.
6. Make the answer more difficult e.g. 10^3, $0.\overset{\bullet}{4}2857\overset{\bullet}{1}$, 37 seconds, 55 ml. etc.
7. The answer is a hexagon/a right angle/a litre/a metre/an inch/one out of four/a bar chart/$3a + b$ . . . etc.

Blockbusters

NAT 1	NAT 2	NAT 5
2 3 4	2 3 4	2 3 4 5 6

EQUIPMENT

Counters of different colours
Dice
Hexagonal paper to make board
Worksheet 2 (page 79)

INSTRUCTIONS

Use the worksheet.

VARIATIONS

1. Make a much larger board (20 × 20 or more). Ask the pupils to work out how many of each possible answer there needs to be, and discuss where is the best place to put them. Should the 'harder' numbers go near the middle or on the edge? etc.
2. Use three dice, or four. What are all the possible answers now? Re-arrange the board accordingly.
3. Play this larger, more complicated game with more people.

REFERENCES

1. The TV Programme – *Blockbusters*
2. "Something to do" by Jan Thomas, Somerset Support Teacher, 1987

Boat

NAT 1	NAT 2
2 3 4 5 6	2 3 4

EQUIPMENT

Throw away materials e.g. cartons, lolly sticks, egg boxes, fertilizer bags, plastic bottles, etc.
Glue
Sellotape
Stapler
Scissors

INSTRUCTIONS

1. 'Design a boat or raft which will carry one person.
2. You are only allowed to use disposable materials to make it, nothing must be bought for the purpose.
3. You are only allowed to use glue, tape and/or staples for fixing it together.
4. Write down detailed instructions so that someone else could build it for you, (write measurements).
5. If you can collect all the materials, build it and test it.'

VARIATIONS

Have a regatta!

Bridges

NAT 1	NAT 2
2 3 4	3 5

EQUIPMENT

Height cards ⎫
Destination Cards ⎬ made from blank playing cards
Reg. No. cards ⎭

Four A4 sheets photocopied up to A3, coloured-in and fitted together to make the board (pages 14–17). (It is then necessary to mount it on something which is soft enough to stick pins in – I use insulation board)
Pins with the registration numbers attached (like flags), to represent lorries
2 dice (Games 2–5)
A set of 'Chance Cards' (Games 3–5)
Coloured cubes (Game 4)
Cubes labelled as various items (Game 5)
Sheet of rules (pages 18–20)

INSTRUCTIONS

Either fill in the height restrictions on the board before it is to be used, or get the players to fill them in before starting the game. It is not as easy as it looks to make everywhere accessible but not too accessible!

The heights I use are as follows:

Top left quarter: starting from top left, clockwise, 14'11", 14'10", 11'7", 12'3", 13'4", 13'4", 12'3".

Top right quarter: top to bottom, 11'2", 15', 10'3".

Bottom right quarter: top 11'6", middle row 14'11", 12'8", 13'8", bottom row 14'2", 11'7".

Bottom left quarter: starting from bottom right, clockwise: 13'3", 15', 10'7", 15'6", 12'7", 13'11".

Follow the sheets of rules.

CARDS FOR BRIDGES GAME

SET 1			SET 2	SET 3
DESTINATION			REGISTRATION NO.	HEIGHT
Dune	1		G666 DEM – colour 1	3.2 m
Dune (wide load)	1		B864 RAT – colour 1	3.4 m
Eelmarsh	1		F841 ORU – colour 1	3.6 m
Frogchester	1		BRU 55W – colour 1	3.8 m
Frogmouth	1		VTR 778T – colour 1	4 m
Ripple	1	Area 1		4.1 m
Rockness	1		FRA 162N – colour 2	4.2 m
Sedge	1		GMT 903Y – colour 2	4.3 m
Spawnvale	1		ORU 801X – colour 2	4.4 m
Spawnvale (wide load)	1		A99 UFO – colour 2	4.5 m
Stillwater	1		D678 KKT – colour 2	
Brownpool	2			10'5"
Brownpool (wide load)	2		C336 TUC – colour 3	11'5"
Croak	2		F939 OPR – colour 3	12'4"
Frogington	2		H522 SIM – colour 3	12'8"
Great Hopping	2	Area 2	BOB 428V – colour 3	12'11"
Little Hopping	2		E927 HAT – colour 3	13'1"
Lower Newty	2			13'6"
Tadborne	2			13'8"
Tadford	2			14'
Upper Newty	2			14'6"
Upper Newty (wide load)	2			
Pebbledash	3			
Pebbledash (wide load)	3			
Pond	3			
Rushey	3			
Sandcastle	3			
Toadley Magna	3	Area 3		
Toadley Magna (wide load)	3			
Toadley Parva	3			
Toadley Parva (wide load)	3			
Wartborough	3			
Wartborough (wide load)	3			

33 CARDS   15 CARDS   20 CARDS

CONVERSION CHART FOR BRIDGES GAME

3 m   = 9'10"
3.1 m = 10'2"
3.2 m = 10'6"
3.3 m = 10'10"
3.4 m = 11'2"
3.5 m = 11'6"
3.6 m = 11'10"
3.7 m = 12'2"
3.8 m = 12'6"
3.9 m = 12'10"
4 m   = 13'2"
4.1 m = 13'6"
4.2 m = 13'10"
4.3 m = 14'1"
4.4 m = 14'5"
4.5 m = 14'9"

CHANCE CARDS　　(Games 3, 4 and 5)

GOOD

Axle weight restrictions lifted	have an extra go
You find a short cut	move on 10 miles
*Road widening completed	ignore any width restrictions
*Message from base	omit 1 destination
Traffic lights stuck on green	have 2 extra goes
New section of dual carriageway	double your next score
New flyover	move on 16 miles
Everyone watching "The Princess and the Frog" on T.V. – roads clear	add 2 to every throw from now on
A bridge has been demolished	choose 1 bridge to ignore
Your lorry has a tune-up	have an extra throw next time you reach a hill
Police roadblock	extra go if lorry less than 4 years old

BAD

Traffic accident	lose a go
*Stuck behind combine harvester	deduct 2 from every throw until next destination
Road flooded	deduct 2 from next throw
Tachograph check	lose a go
Overweight at weighbridge	go back to last town
Urgent message from base	add Rockness to your journey
Rockslide blocks road	lose 2 goes
Cattle crossing	deduct 4 from next go
Level crossing	lose a go
Roadworks traffic lights	next throw only use 1 die
Slippery road	deduct 3 from next go
Bumpy road surface	move 1 mile only on next go
Fallen tree	go back 6 miles
Loose chippings	deduct 2 from next go
Puncture	lose 2 goes
Police roadblock	lose a go if lorry over 5 years old

SUGGESTED ITEMS FOR COLLECTION (Game 5)

bags of coal	2 points	(must **not** be carried with the coats, bed or carpets)
fur coats	7 points	
an antique table	10 points	(**must** be carried on its own)
3-piece suite	3 points	(**must** be in the same lorry as the bed)
a fridge	1 point	
fresh fish	2 points	(**must** be loaded last because it makes everything else smell!)
a microwave oven	6 points	
bags of fertiliser	4 points	(loaded last again!)
dangerous chemicals	5 points	(may **only** go with coal, fridge, sand, freezer or whisky)
a garden shed	3 points	
second-hand books ..	1 point	
a bed	2 points	(**must** be in the same lorry as the 3-piece suite)
a freezer	4 points	
cases of whisky	8 points	
Christmas trees	2 points	(**not** in the same lorry as the table)
a boat	7 points	(if you pick this up you only have room for 4 more items)

bags of sand	1 point	
a computer	5 points	
scientific equipment	9 points	(**must** be loaded first to prevent breakage)
nets of cabbages	3 points	
carpets	3 points	
cage of rare monkeys	11 points	(must **not** be carried in the same lorry as the cabbages or fish)

Example of
Height cards

12' 11"   **3.8 m**

Example of
Registration number cards

E927 HAT   **VTR 778T**

Example of
Destination cards

Pebbledash   **Dune >Wide Load<**

Example of
Chance cards

Bumpy road surface.

Move one mile only on your next go.

Loose chippings, slow down in case your windscreen breaks. Deduct 2 from your next go.

Traffic lights are stuck on green.

Have 2 extra goes.

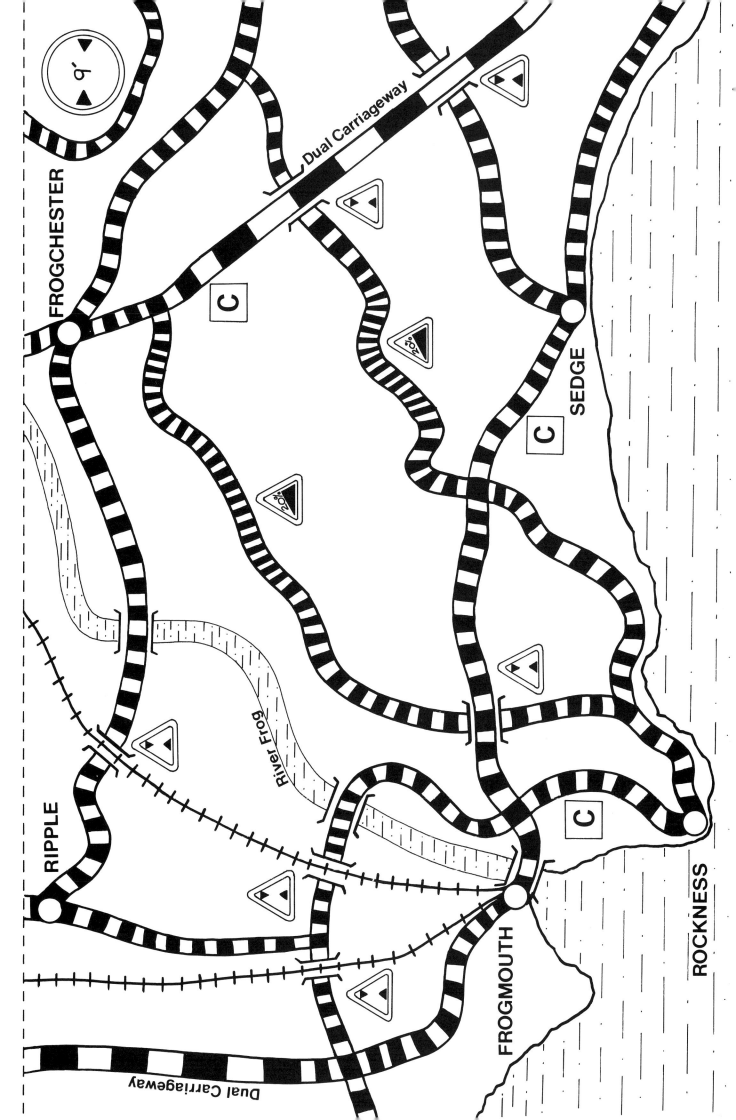

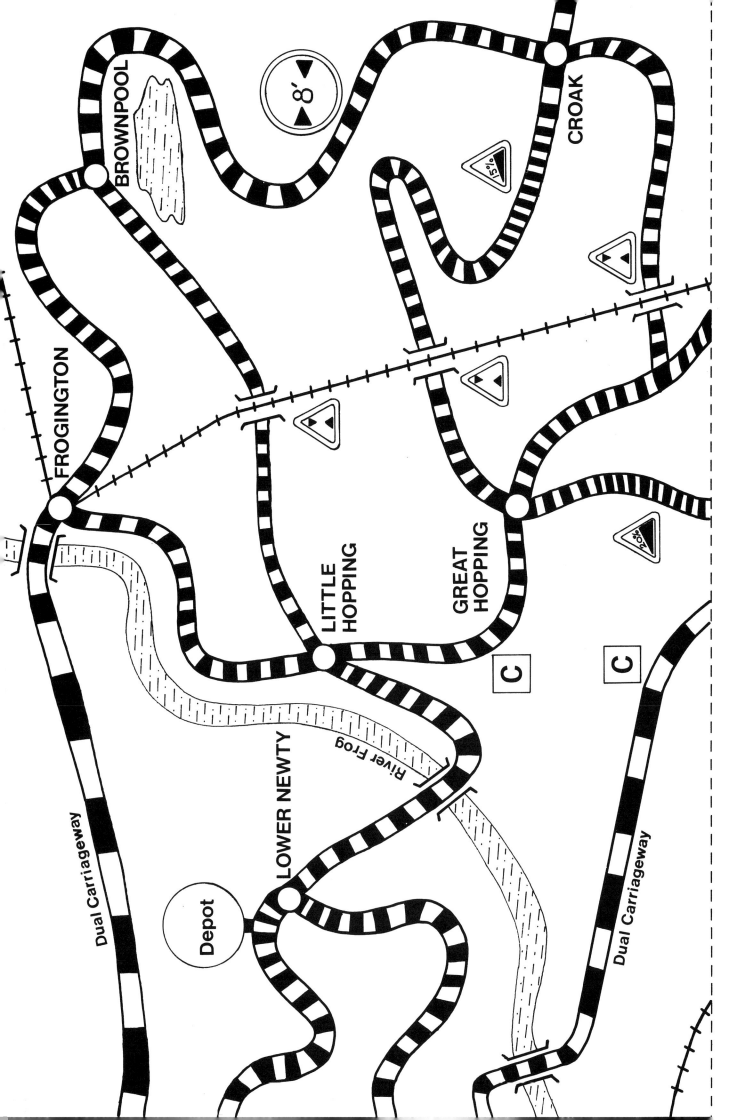

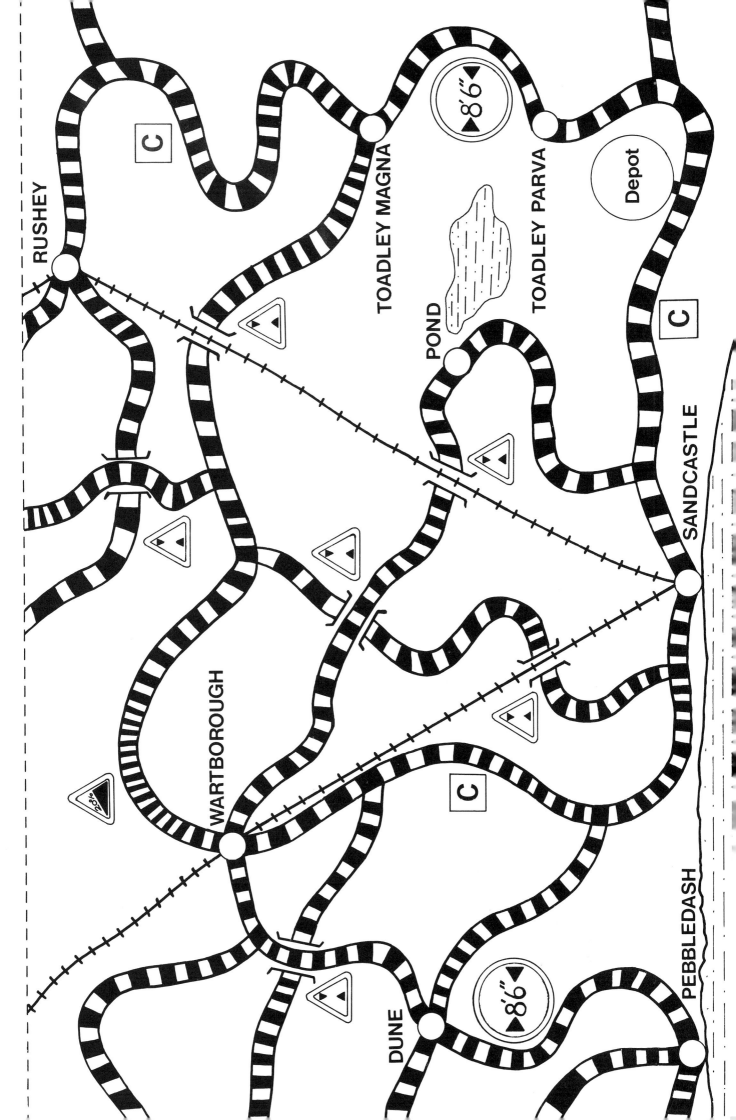

BRIDGES Game 1

Rules

A game for 2–6 players
1. Put the lorries in their home depots (according to colour).
2. Place the three packs of cards (height, destination, registration number) face down where everyone can reach them.
3. Choose a score-keeper and give him or her paper and pencil.
4. Decide who will go first.
5. Player 1 picks up one card from each pack. These will tell him or her which lorry to use, the height of its load and its destination.
6. Player 1 then has a set time (depending on age/ability, say 30 seconds) in which to find the shortest route to that destination.
7. Leave the lorry there, don't return it to the depot.
8. The other players check the route to see if it really is the shortest.
9. If they agree it is the shortest, the player scores one point and Player 2 has a turn.
10. If another player can see a shorter route, he or she makes a challenge. The two players count up the mileage of their routes (every white section of road counts as a mile.) The player with the shorter route gets the point.
11. If either the player or the challenger is spotted going under a bridge which is too low for the lorry, or turning off where they can't, then they are fined two points.
12. Used cards go on the bottom of the packs after each go.
13. If you pick up a destination card which shows the position of your lorry at the start (no journey would be necessary) discard it and pick again.
14. The first player to reach 10 points is the winner.

BRIDGES Game 2

Rules

A game for 2–6 players
1. Put the lorries in their home depots.
2. Each player takes 1 registration number card   1 load height card
                       3 destination cards (1 from each area pack)
   (To make the game longer you could take 2 destination cards from each area pack.)
3. The picked cards are placed face up in front of each player.
4. If, on the longer game, you pick up 2 cards with the same destination, discard one and pick again.
5. Your aim is to visit each of your 3 (or 6) destinations and then return the lorry to any depot.
6. You must plan a route which avoids any bridges whose clearance is less than your load height.
7. Player 1 rolls two dice and the total tells how many miles he or she can move. (Each white road section represents 1 mile.)
8. If you roll a double you have an extra go.
9. Player 2 then has a go and so on.
10. Each time you reach one of your destinations, turn that card face down. This is so that the other players can see how far you have got on your journey.
11. The height restriction applies to the whole journey until you make your last call. After that the lorry is unloaded and you can ignore height restrictions on the way back to a depot.
12. If another player spots you trying to go under a bridge which is too low or turn off where you can't, then you lose a go (you have knocked the load off and have to restack it!)

BRIDGES Game 3

Rules

A game for 2–6 players

Rules 1 to 11 are the same as for Game 2.

12. If any of your destination cards says 'WIDE LOAD' you cannot go along roads with a width restriction until you have made your last call and your lorry is empty. If you are caught breaking this rule you lose a go and you have to go back and find a correct route.

13. If you pass a large letter C, you must pick up a Chance Card.

BRIDGES Game 4

Rules

A game for 2–6 players

1. Put the lorries in their home depots.
2. Shake up the cubes and place one on each town or village. (1 red, 2 blue, 3 green, 3 yellow, 4 orange, 4 brown, 5 white.)
3. Each player takes one registration number card and one load height card, identifies his or her lorry and leaves the height card visible to the other players.
4. The aim is to plan a route around the board picking up the cubes as you go. You do not have to land directly on a town to pick up the cube – passing through is enough.
5. The player who returns to home depot with the most points wins. The cubes have different values:
   red = 7 points
   blue = 6 points
   green = 5 points
   yellow = 4 points
   orange = 3 points
   brown = 2 points
   white = 1 point.
6. Your route must avoid any bridges whose clearance is less than your load height. This applies to the whole journey.
   Rules 7, 8 and 9 are the same as for Game 2.
10. If another player spots you trying to go under a bridge which is too low or turn off where you can't, then you lose a go (you have knocked the roof off your lorry or cracked the sump).
11. If you pass a large letter C, you must pick up a Chance card. (The cards marked * must be removed from the pack for this game as their rewards/penalties are irrelevant.)

BRIDGES Game 5

Rules

A game for 2–6 players

1. Put the lorries in their home depots.
2. Shake up the bag of items for collection and place one on each town or village.
3. Each player takes one registration number card and one load height card, identifies his or her lorry and leaves the height card visible to the other players.
4. The aim is to plan a route around the board picking up the items as you go.
5. You can pass through a town without picking an item up if it's something you don't want.
6. If you do want an item you forfeit any extra moves you might throw. For example, you are 6 miles away from a village where you want to pick up something and you throw 5 and 3: you move the 6 miles, load up and stay put, losing the extra 2 miles.
7. You can unload unwanted items but only at a town or village which has nothing awaiting collection when you get there. (Again you have to forfeit extra miles.)
8. The player who gets back to his or her depot with the most points wins.
9. You can return to your depot to unload during the game. Any items brought to your own depot cannot be picked up by another player and count towards your final score.
10. Your route must avoid any bridges whose clearance is less than your load height. However, when your lorry is empty you can ignore bridge heights.
11. Player 1 rolls two dice and the total tells how many miles he or she can move. (Each white road section represents 1 mile.)
12. If you roll a double you have an extra go.
13. Player 2 then has a go and so on.
14. If another player spots you trying to go under a bridge which is too low or turn off where you can't, you lose a go. (You've knocked your co-driver unconscious and have to give him first aid.)
15. If you pass a large letter C, you must pick up a Chance card. (The cards marked * must be removed from the pack for this game.)

Car Boot Sales

NAT 1	NAT 2	NAT 5
2 3 4 5	2 3 4 5 6	2 3 4 5

EQUIPMENT

Local newspapers
Paper
Pencil

INSTRUCTIONS

'You've decided to make some money and you have thought of selling something at a car boot sale.

Find out how much it will cost to hire a space.

Do you know someone with a biggish car who would take you? How much will you have to pay them for petrol?

What are you going to collect or make to sell? How much will it cost you? How much will you sell for? How many do you think you'll be able to sell?

Did you make a profit?'

VARIATIONS

'Look at other ways of raising money, e.g. a stall at a fete – what type of stall would you run?'

Car Parking

NAT 1	NAT 2	NAT 3	NAT 5
2 3 4 5	2 3 4	2 3 4 5 6	2 3

EQUIPMENT

Paper
Pen
Card or plastic 5p, 10p, 20p, 50p, £1 coins

INSTRUCTIONS

'A car-park ticket machine takes 5p, 10p, 20p, 50p and £1 coins. You arrive to find that 1 hour will cost 50p. You must put in exactly the right amount. You have an unlimited supply of all coins.

How many different sets of coins can you feed the machine to get your tickets?'

VARIATIONS

1. 'What if the cost of a ticket was 40p, 60p, 30p, 70p? Is there any pattern in the number of ways?
2. A whole day's parking costs £5. How many ways could you pay?
3. What would happen to your results if the *order* in which you used the coins made a difference?
4. A new machine is installed which will give change. (If you put in £1 for an hour it will release 50p back to you.) How does this affect your results?
5. The machine will not accept the new size 5p coins. How does this affect the results you have found so far?'

Colouring Areas

NAT 2	NAT 3	NAT 4
3 4 5 6	4 5 7 8	2 3 4 5 6 7 8

EQUIPMENT

Colours
Paper
Pencil
Worksheets 3–5 (pages 80–82)

INSTRUCTIONS

I have found these colouring activities a useful way to reinforce equivalence, or to practice fraction work. I try to make the picture difficult to spot, and my drawing is so bad that I usually succeed!

These worksheets use
– fraction calculations
– equivalent fractions
– equivalent fractions, decimals, percentages

because they were made up for specific groups of children for whom these areas caused problems.

I then ask the pupils to make up their own colouring puzzles, warning them not to make the spaces too small, and they enjoy giving their puzzles to others to solve.

VARIATIONS

1. Topology – colour in anything equivalent to a circle.
2. Harder calculations – colour in areas where the answer is . . .
3. Two-D shapes – colour in areas with quadrilaterals.
4. Symmetry – colour in areas with shapes having two lines of symmetry.
5. Include ratios with fractions.
6. Prime numbers (or square numbers, or multiples of 7 etc.).
7. Equations which go through (0, 0).
8. Triangles which are similar or congruent.

Competitions

NAT 1	NAT 2	NAT 3	NAT 5
2 3 4 5	2 3 4 5	2 3 4 5 6	2 3 4

EQUIPMENT

Magazines with competitions in
Mail-shot competitions
Calculator
Bank interest rates

INSTRUCTIONS

'Find examples of competitions where you have a choice between a lump sum and an amount per year, or a car, holiday, etc.

Work out which is better value.

Take interest rates into account.

Does it depend on how old you are? How might inflation affect your answer?'

VARIATIONS

'Find some competitions where you have to put things in order of importance.

Work out how many different orders there are. What are your chances of winning?'

Examples of competition prizes

OFFICIAL PRIZE LIST

£200,000 CASH
OR £1,500 MONTHLY INCOME
if the winning entry is re____ned within 14 days

FIRST PRIZE CHOICE
£15,000 CASH

FIRST PRIZE CHOICE
£1,500 a year for life

SECOND PRIZE

A WEEKEND FOR TWO IN PARIS

2

OR £1,500 CASH

CHOICE OF FIRST PRIZE worth £100,000

To be taken as a single lump sum of £100,000, or as a regular income of £685 a month for life.

Consecutive Numbers

NAT 1	NAT 2	NAT 3
2 3 4 5	2 3 4	2 3 4 5

EQUIPMENT

Paper
Pencil
Calculator (for follow-up game)

INSTRUCTIONS

1. 'What totals do you get by adding pairs of consecutive numbers?
2. What pattern do the totals of three consecutive numbers make?
3. How about 4, 5 . . . etc?
4. Which totals *cannot* be made by the addition of consecutive numbers?
   (Cross out the ones you have already found on a 100 square)
   e.g. $9 = 2 + 3 + 4$
   $10 = 1 + 2 + 3 + 4$
   $11 = 5 + 6$
   $12 = 3 + 4 + 5$
   $13 = 6 + 7$
   so all these *can* be made.'

VARIATIONS

When the pupils have investigated this, and listed the ones which they can't find (and maybe identified them as powers of 2) then a game could be devised giving any high number and seeing who is the first to find out from which consecutive numbers it can be made. Pupils can work in teams, using calculators. Ask them to write down their strategies for finding an answer – compare strategies.

Dart Scores

NAT 1	NAT 2
2 3 4	2 3 4

EQUIPMENT

Picture of a dart board
Paper
Pencil

INSTRUCTIONS

Investigate dart scores:

'Assuming all three darts hit the board (unlike mine which tend to do a double somersault and then bury themselves in the ceiling or the marker's arm) what's the lowest score you can get? What's the highest? How many ways can you do this?

Can you score 179? Which scores are impossible? How many ways can you score 40? (e.g. 20, 10, 10/20, double 5, 10/treble 5, 20, 5/ double 10, 10, double 5/17, 15, 8/25, 10, 5 etc.)

Which score can be achieved in the most different ways? (Look at single numbers first and then add the doubles, and then the trebles.)

If you are playing 301 and have to start and finish with a double, what is the least number of darts you could use? What about 401 or 501 etc?

You are allowed seven darts for 301 (double start and finish). How many ways could you do it?'

VARIATIONS

1. 'What would you score if you threw a dart in each number in turn (not scoring doubles or trebles)?
2. What would you score if you went round the board scoring only doubles?
3. What would you score if you went round in trebles?
4. What would you score if you threw Shanghais only? (A Shanghai consists of a single, double and treble of a number.)
5. A "good" player can hit the number he aims at – which number is his best?
6. An "average" player can get within one either side – which number should he aim at?
7. A "poor" player can only be sure of getting a dart within two segments, either side of the one he throws at. Which number should he aim at?'

Decision Trees

NAT 2	NAT 3	NAT 4	NAT 5
3 4 5	5 7 8	3 4 5 6 8 9	4

EQUIPMENT

Card
Scissors
Solid shapes
Plain shapes

INSTRUCTIONS

Choose one of the suggested decision trees and make up a large wall display where the decision boxes are drawn but empty and the statements or objects are correctly sorted at the bottom, an example is given here.

Ask the pupils if they can work out what questions must have been in each box. If they find this too difficult, or as a check when they have done it, give out the 12 questions and ask them to put them in the appropriate spaces.

Either move straight on to getting the pupils to construct their own decision trees or do another one where you have already constructed it and they have to work out the questions which were posed.

SUGGESTED DECISION TREES
1. Make up a decision tree diagram to sort a collection of solid shapes.
2. Make up a decision tree diagram to sort shapes which have line and/or rotational symmetry of different orders.
3. Make up a decision tree diagram to sort these numbers: 41, 42, 49, 55, 60, 64, 100.
4. Make up a decision tree diagram to sort: Km, millilitre, Kg, balance, ruler, scales, tape-measure, inch, gallon, clock, acre, hour, hectare, mile, stopwatch, ounce, protractor, degree, thermometer, etc.
5. Think up a few more statements such as:
   a) Tomorrow I will turn into a giant frog.
   b) I will pick out a blue cube from a bag containing 3 red and 3 blue cubes.
   c) Tomorrow I will be older than today.
   and then draw a decision tree diagram to sort them.
6. Write out a lot of equations and sort them using questions such as:
   a) does it produce a straight line?
   b) does it produce two lines?
   c) is it written in terms of x?
   d) does it go through (0, 0)? etc.
7. Sorting triangles for similarity and congruence.

Pupils might also enjoy putting their decision trees into "Sorting Game" and making up puzzles for others to solve. (This program is from the M.E.S.U. Information – Handling Pack produced by the National Council for Education Technology, Sir William Lyons Road, Science Park, University of Warwick, Coventry CV4 7EZ.)

Example of cards for a decision tree for sorting quadrilaterals

Has it any right angles?	Has it two pairs of equal sides?	Are all its sides the same length?
Has it two equal sides?	Has it two pairs of parallel lines?	Has it any parallel lines?
Has it two pairs of equal sides?	Is it concave?	Has it two equal sides?
Has it any right angles?	Has it four right angles?	Are all its sides the same length?

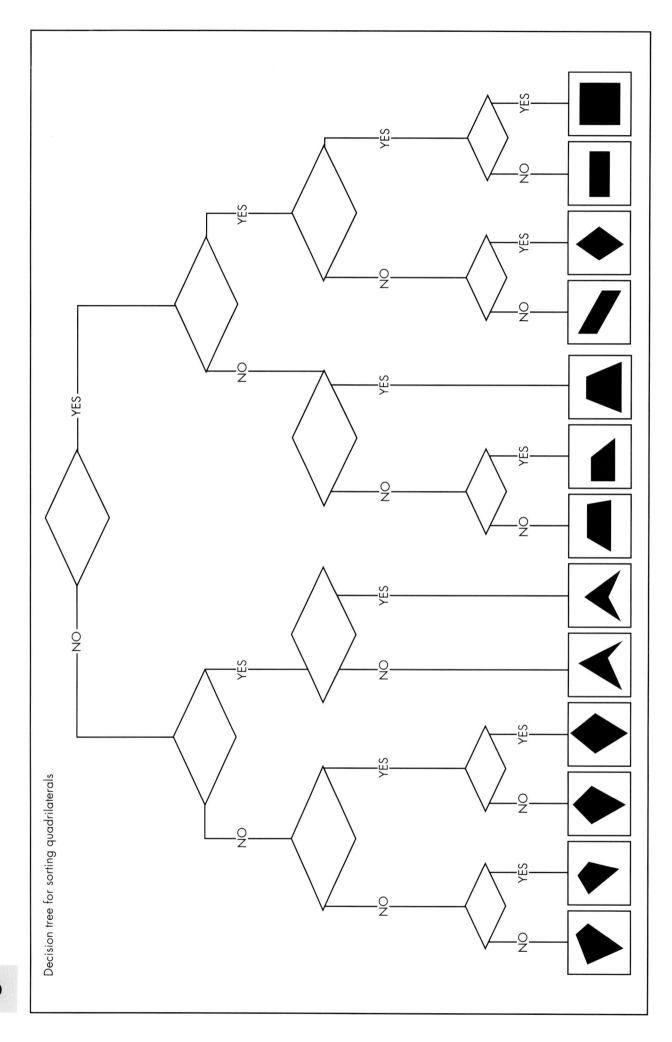

Decision tree for sorting quadrilaterals

Design a Car-park.

NAT 1	NAT 2	NAT 4	NAT 5
2 3 4	2 3 4	4 5 6 7	2 3 4 5

EQUIPMENT

Paper (plain/graph/squared)
Pencil
Car sales brochures/car magazines
Tape measure

INSTRUCTIONS

'Given a set area (e.g. 100 m² which could be 10m × 10m or 50m × 2m etc.) design the best single storey car-park you can. Think about:

1. The length, width and height of cars to be parked. What about trucks?
2. The turning circle of various cars. If this information is not available in the brochures or magazines perhaps you can test the staff cars? How would you do this?
3. Exit and entrance.
   Draw your car-park to scale.
   Explain why you designed it as you did and why it is better than other alternatives.'

VARIATIONS

'You now have the money to build another floor. How would your design need altering so that you have two floors of 100 m² each? Would it house twice as many cars as your first design?'

Dominoes

NAT 2	NAT 4
3 4 5 6 7 8	3 4 5 9

EQUIPMENT

Blank playing cards to make set of dominoes

INSTRUCTIONS

A game for 2–4 players.

1. Deal all the cards.
2. The person with the highest value double card plays first.
3. Double cards are laid sideways.
4. Play as in normal dominoes by placing a matching card at either end. (You cannot go sideways on double cards.)
5. The winner is the first to lay all the cards.
6. If no one finishes, use the value card to see how many points you have left in your hand. The winner is the one with the least points. Or use these points as a cumulative total over several games.'

VARIATIONS

Dominoes can be made for:

1. Fractions, decimals, percentages and ratios.
2. Imperial/metric measurements and or metric equivalents.
3. 24 hour clock/12 hour clock/digital and analogue displays.
4. Topology.
5. Mixed calculations (as difficult as you like).

6. Symmetry.
7. Congruence.

Dominoes and other card games like snap are very useful, as you can make up sets of varying difficulty so that the whole class are doing the same thing but at a level where they can all cope.

METHOD FOR MAKING DOMINOES

Choose the number of alternatives you want to use, thus determining the size of the pack.

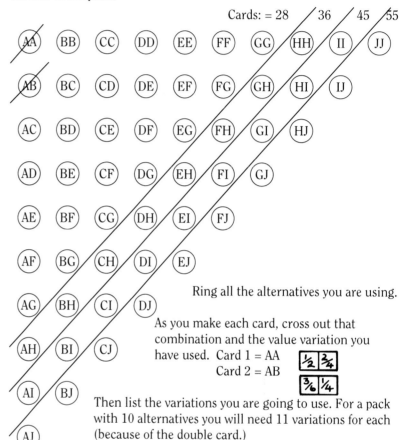

Cards: = 28 / 36 / 45 / 55

Ring all the alternatives you are using.

As you make each card, cross out that combination and the value variation you have used. Card 1 = AA
Card 2 = AB

Then list the variations you are going to use. For a pack with 10 alternatives you will need 11 variations for each (because of the double card.)

	A	B	C	D	E	F	G	H	I	J
1	½	¼	¾	⅓	⅔	⅙	⅛	1/10	1/12	1/9
2	¾	⅔8	6/8	2/6	4/6	2/12	2/16	2/20	2/24	2/18
3	⅜	3/12	9/12	3/9	6/9	3/18	3/24	3/30	3/36	3/27
4	4/8	4/16	12/16	4/12	8/12	4/24	4/32	4/40	4/48	4/36
5	5/10	5/20	15/20	5/15	10/15	5/30	5/40	5/50	5/60	5/45
6	6/12	6/24	18/24	6/18	12/18	6/36	6/48	6/60	6/72	9/81
7	7/14	7/28	21/23	7/21	40/60	8/48	10/80	7/70	10/120	10/90
8	10/20	10/40	30/40	10/30	20/30	10/60	20/160	8/80	12/144	11/99
9	25/50	25/100	75/100	33/99	66/99	11/66	25/200	9/90	20/240	20/180
10	30/60	30/120	90/120	40/120	80/120	50/300	50/400	10/100	25/300	100/900
11	50/100	50/200	150/200	50/150	100/150	100/600	100/800	100/1000	50/600	50/450

Difficult set: eleven different variations for each alternative.

Example of
   'Topological dominoes' using
   equivalence.

Example of
   domino pack based on the
   question 'How many lines of
   symmetry?'

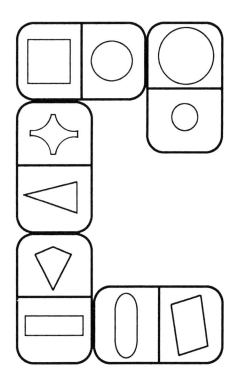

Example of
domino pack using equivalents within and between a variety of metric and imperial measurements.

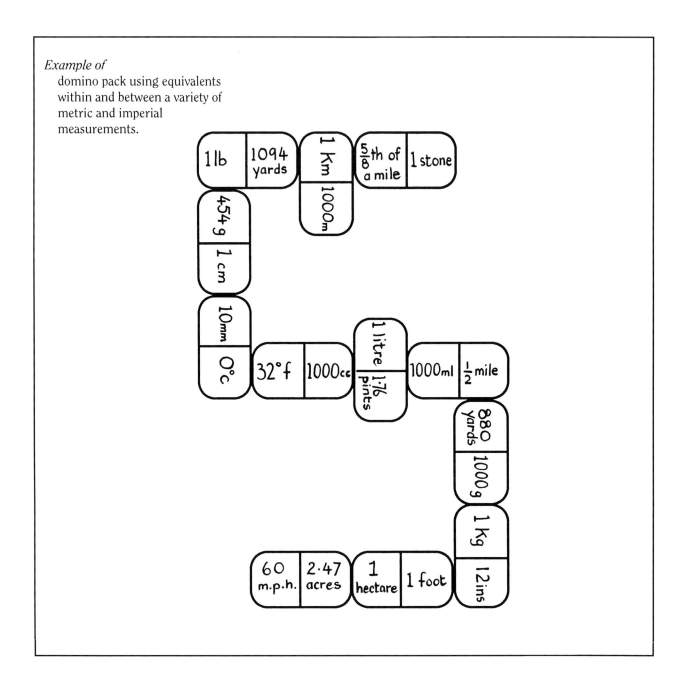

Eeny meeny miny mo

EQUIPMENT

Pencil
Paper
Wedding (Belle's) story (page 32)

INSTRUCTIONS

1. 'Choose a playground rhyme which doesn't involve a random element. (One potato/eeny meeny/Itt ditt etc.)
2. Decide whether when someone is out you continue round the circle or start again at the first person (continuing round works better).
3. Find out who will be chosen if there are only two people to choose between or if there are three, or four etc. Is there a position to avoid if you don't want to be chosen? Or a position to favour if you *do* want to be chosen?
4. Now try a different rhyme.'

VARIATIONS

This is quite a complex investigation. For a simpler starter use the 'Wedding (Belle's) story. Act it out.

The program is for cheating teachers who want to check pupils' results!

This is a computer print out of a program in 'Basic' for a BBC computer.

```
10PRINT"THIS PROGRAM WILL TELL YOU WHO WILL BE"
20PRINT"SELECTED FROM A CIRCLE OF PEOPLE"
30PRINT"USING A RHYME LIKE"
40PRINT"   ___ EENY, MEENY, MINY, MO ___"
50PRINT
60PRINT"HOW MANY BEATS ARE THERE IN YOUR RHYME?"
70PRINT"_____ (3 TO 30) _____"
80INPUT B
90IFB>30 PRINT"I DON'T THINK A RHYME THIS LENGTH WOULD BE MUCH GOOD"
100IFB>30 PRINT"_ IT'D BE DARK!"
110IFB>30 PRINT "BY THE TIME YOU STARTED THE GAME!":GOTO 100
120IFB<3 PRINT "TOO SHORT FOR A RHYME; BE SENSIBLE!":GOTO 100
130DIM Y(45)
140Y(2)=(B MOD 2)+1
150*FX6
160VDU2
170PRINT "FOR 2 PEOPLE THE ONE SELECTED WOULD BE NUMBER";Y(2)
180FOR P=3 TO 40
190 IF P<B THEN PROCunderbeat(P)
200IF P=B THEN PROCsamebeat(P)
210IFP>B THEN PROCoverbeat(P)
220PRINT"FOR ";P;" PEOPLE THE ONE SELECTED WOULD BE NUMBER";Y(P)
230NEXT P
240VDU3
250END
260DEF PROCunderbeat(P)
270R=B MOD P
280X=1
290Y(P)=R+Y(P-1)
300IF Y(P)>P THEN Y(P)=Y(P)-P
310ENDPROC
320DEF PROCsamebeat(P)
330Y(B)=Y(B-1)
340ENDPROC
350DEF PROCoverbeat(P)
360R=P MOD B
370X=P DIV B
380A=Y(P-X)
390Y(P)=B*X+A
400IFY(P)>P THEN Y(P)=(A-R)+(A-R)DIV(B-1)
410IF (A-R)MOD(B-1)=0 THEN Y(P)=Y(P)-1
420ENDPROC
```

WEDDING (BELLE'S)

King Nicholas the Nasty only had one child, a daughter called Belle. This was because he was so nasty his wife had very soon run off with a dragon. (The dragon breathed fire at her occasionally and forgot to cut his claws, but on the whole it was much nicer than living with Nicholas the Nasty).

The Princess grew up to be very beautiful like her mother, but she could also be stubborn and bad-tempered like her father. When she was 18 her father invited all the important families in the kingdom to a banquet, hoping that one of the sons would ask for his daughter's hand. Several of them would have done, because she had quite a pretty hand, but Belle didn't like any of them and so was as rude to them as possible. When he heard her the King flew into a terrible temper and started throwing sausage rolls and jellies. The Princess was just as angry as her father and replied by showering him with jam tarts and rock cakes. The guests had to dodge the flying food and get out as best they could. (The young men decided that the next time they went hand-offering they'd get a psychiatrist's report done first.)

When Belle was 21 the King invited the not-so-important families to a barbeque (the important ones wouldn't come near the castle any more), but the day went along similar lines: the King and Princess ended up bombarding each other with spare ribs and beefburgers. The guests made off across the rockery or through the goldfish pond.

Eventually Nicholas got really Nasty. He summoned Belle to his room. 'It's time you were married. I'm going to round up a bunch of men from the market place, lock them in the Hall and you will choose one,' he shouted.

The Princess stamped her foot and refused.

'In that case,' roared the King, 'I'll stand them in a circle and my executioner will cut off the head of every other man he comes to until there's only one left. Then you'll have *no* choice, you'll marry that one!'

The King stomped off to get his guards. The Princess ran quickly to the stables where Sidney the Slave was mucking out the yard. Sid was the man she really wanted to marry and now her dreams could come true. She told him of her father's plan, jumping up and down with happiness.

'All you have to do is go to the market place and get rounded up, and then when the executioner comes, just work out where to stand so that you're the last one left alive!'

'Er . . . um . . . yes', said Sid.

I think he might need a bit of help!

Estimating Activities

NAT 2
2 3 4

EQUIPMENT

Some of the following: clear plastic containers with various numbers of beads, beans, peas, washers etc. (anything which is a constant size)

Empty containers of various volumes

Packages of different weights

Kitchen scales, bathroom scales

Rulers and tape measures

Trundle wheel

Stopwatch

Thermometer

Groups of same sized objects e.g. multilink cubes, biros, chalks, baked bean tins, Oxo cubes, sheets of papers, clothes pegs, etc.

Pupils' answer sheet

Teacher's answer sheet

REFERENCES

Variation 2 courtesy of Brian Tillbrook.

INSTRUCTIONS

1. Divide the class into six groups and give each group a copy of the pupils' answer sheet.
2. Ask a question from the list and get the groups to decide on their estimate and write it in the estimate column.
3. Collect in their estimates (in a different order each time so that one group isn't always first or last), and fill them in on your sheet.
4. A pupil then measures the subject of the question, or you announce the answer if it is one measured beforehand.
5. Pupils fill in the actual answer in the 'Answer' column.
6. Award 6 points to the group whose estimate was closest, 5 to the next, down to 1 point to the furthest away.
7. Pupils record the points awarded and total those at the end to find the winning group.

VARIATIONS

1. This method is quicker, but the pupils do not get the chance to do any measuring, as everything is measured by you before the lesson.
   a) Ask the questions and pupils write down their estimates.
   b) Announce the limits and scores, e.g. 'if you're within 5 you get 4 points, within 15 you get 1 point.'
   c) Pupils call out their answers, you note down the scores and then tell the groups the correct answer and what they have scored.
2. a) All the items to be estimated are listed on a sheet and apparatus placed around the room.
   b) Pupils fill in their estimates and hand in completed sheets.
   c) While you mark their sheets the pupils collect measuring equipment and go round measuring the items.
   d) Pupils get papers back with points awarded and compare their answers with yours.

QUESTIONS FOR ESTIMATING ACTIVITIES

How many beans/washers/grains of rice do you think there are in each container?

How much water will it take to fill this container? (in pints or in litres)

When it is full of water how much do you think it will weigh? (in lb or oz or g or kg)

How much do you think this package/my briefcase/this brick/Fred Bloggs weighs? (imperial or metric units specified)

How long do you think this pencil/the table/the classroom/the gym/the playing field is? (imperial or metric)

How tall do you think your teacher/the door is?

How far is it from John's knee to his ankle/across Ann's shoulders/round Mary's head?

How long do you think it will take someone (specified) to count to 100/count from 50 backwards/say the alphabet/say the 8 times table/touch their toes 30 times/make a 5 × 5 × 5 cube out of multilink cubes?

How long do you think someone (specified) can hold their breath/stand on one leg with hands on head/balance a board ruler upright on one finger?

Here are 20 sheets of paper. How high will a stack of 1000 be? (in in. or cm)

Here are some biros. If I laid 50 of them end to end how many metres (or yards or feet) do you think they'd stretch?

Here are 10 multilink cubes fixed in a line. How long would a line of 500 cubes be? (in metres or yards)

If I placed 100 pieces of chalk side by side like this [ ] how many cm or in. would they reach?

Here is a baked bean tin. If a supermarket has a stack of them 20 high how many feet/metres high is this?

Here are 5 clothespegs on a line [ ] How much line would 300 of them cover? (imperial or metric)

Here is an Oxo cube. How much do you think 24 of them would weigh (in oz or gm)

Here is an orange. A sack of 40 would weigh how many pounds/kg?

What do you think the temperature is in the classroom/outside in °C or °F?

Teacher's answer sheet format:

ESTIMATING ACTIVITIES

	Group 1		Group 2		Group 3		Group 4		Group 5		Group 6	
	Est.	Pts.	Est.	Pts.	Est.	Pts.	Est.	Pts.	Est.	Pts.	Est.	Pts.
1												
2												
3												
4												
etc.												

Pupils' Answer sheet format:

Question Number	Units of Measurement	Estimate	Answer	Points
1				
2				
3				
4				
etc.				

Factor Chains

NAT 1	NAT 2	NAT 3
2 3 4	3 4 7	2 3 4 5 6

EQUIPMENT

Paper
Pencil

INSTRUCTIONS

'Choose any number, say 16. Add together all its factors except for the number itself: $1 + 2 + 4 + 8 = 15$. Do the same to the new number: $1 + 3 + 5 = 9$. And again . . . etc.

Investigate chains of this type

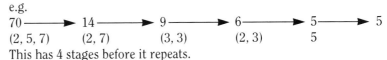

$$16 \longrightarrow 15 \longrightarrow 9 \longrightarrow \text{etc.}$$
$$(1, 2, 4, 8) \quad\quad (1, 3, 5) \quad\quad (1, 3)$$

Add factors except
number itself

Do you see any patterns?
What happens when you start with 6?
Do any other numbers behave like 6?'

VARIATIONS

1. What happens if you add all the factors except the number itself and one, each time? Who can find the longest chain?
2. Using the *prime* factors who can find the longest chain?
   e.g.
   $$70 \longrightarrow 14 \longrightarrow 9 \longrightarrow 6 \longrightarrow 5 \longrightarrow 5$$
   $$(2, 5, 7) \quad (2, 7) \quad (3, 3) \quad (2, 3) \quad 5$$
   This has 4 stages before it repeats.

Feathers and Bricks

NAT 1	NAT 2
2 3 4	2 3 6

EQUIPMENT

Aquarium pebbles or sand
Plastic bags
Sticky labels or permanent felt pens
A brick
A feather (or more)
Balance scales
A weight (200 g perhaps)
Pebbles

INSTRUCTIONS

'Using the apparatus provided and nothing else, find the weight of:
1. a brick
2. a feather
Write down how you got your answer.
How many times heavier is a brick than a feather?
Could you now find the weights of e.g. a ruler or a book more quickly?
Explain how. Can you think of any other methods of doing this?'

VARIATIONS

1. 'You know how much a feather weighs . . . How many feathers do you think are on an average chicken? How much would they weigh? How much do you think its insides weigh? So how much weight is lost in plucking and gutting?

2. How many bricks can a bricklayer carry at once with just his hands? Or when using a hod? How much weight is this?
3. Write to duvet/sleeping bag manufacturers and ask how they measure togs. Is it the weight/density/type of filling which matters?'

Find the Division

NAT 2	NAT 3
3 4 6	4

EQUIPMENT

Calculator
Paper
Pencil

INSTRUCTIONS

'I divided a number by another number. Both numbers were less than 100. The answer came to 0.597701 on my calculator. Can you find out which two numbers I used?

Choose two numbers yourself and divide one by the other to make up a puzzle for someone else.'

VARIATIONS

Restrict to numbers less than 20.

'How many tries did you have before you found my answer? Did you record each one? If not, record them next time and then try to write down a good strategy for solving this type of problem.'

Four Fours

NAT 2
2 3 4 5

EQUIPMENT

Paper
Pen
Calculator

INSTRUCTIONS

'Construct a way of representing each integer from 1–10 using four 4s and any operation; $+ - \times \div \sqrt{\ }$.'

VARIATIONS

1. 'Extend to 20, 50, 100.
2. Make negative numbers.
3. 'Use the digits of your telephone number, in order, to make the answers 1 to 100, using $+ - \times \div$ and brackets.
   e.g. if your number is 0202 884216

   then $0 \times 202884216 = 0$

   $((020 + 28 - 8) \div 4 \div 2 + 1) \div 6 = 1$

   $(020 + (2 \times 8) - (8 \times 4)) \times 2 - (1 \times 6) = 2$

   etc.
4. Use today's date: 26.10.1991
   e.g. $(261 \times 0) + 1 + 9 - 9 - 1 = 0$

   $2 + 6 + 1 + (0 \times 19) - 9 + 1 = 1$

   $2 + 6 + 10 + 1 - 9 - 9 + 1 = 2$ etc.

Fred's Bread

NAT 1	NAT 2
2 3 4 5	2 3 4 5 6

EQUIPMENT

Paper
Pencil
Counters or squares of paper to show sites
Squared paper
Worksheet 6 (page 83)

INSTRUCTIONS

Give out copies of the worksheet.

'This is the plan of a new estate. Each block is square and every corner site has been reserved for shops and businesses. Fred is a baker. He has been allocated three sites where he can open bread shops: one on the corner of Crackpot and Dracula, one on Ghoul/Horror corner and one on Rhubarb/Loony. He has free choice of position for his bakery. Each day he will have to deliver a full van-load of bread and cakes to each shop, returning from each shop to the bakery to reload. Investigate different sites for the bakery (Fred is worried about his petrol bill!)

Are there several economical sites or only one? Change the position of his shops and look at where to put the bakery now. It may be a good idea to consider two shops only to begin with and then try more.

Can you find a rule to cover each number of shops? Is there a rule to cope with any number of shops?'

VARIATIONS

1. The plan of the new estate could have rectangular blocks.
2. Or triangular blocks.
3. Other grids.
4. Fred buys a large lorry and can deliver daily to each shop without returning to the bakery to reload.

Golf Balls

NAT 1	NAT 2	NAT 4	NAT 5
2 3 4	3	2 3 4 5 7 8	2 3 4

EQUIPMENT

Golf balls
Sugar paper
Scissors
Ruler
Card
Felt pens and coloured pencils
Glue/sellotape
Compasses
Selection of commercial packaging of different shapes
Flattened nets of various boxes

INSTRUCTIONS

'A firm which makes sporting equipment is trying to increase its sales of golf balls. A questionnaire sent to golf clubs has shown that golfers would prefer to buy their balls in packs of four. The design department is given the job of making eye-catching packs to hold four golf balls. They will be made of cardboard. You are one of the people told to think up a new design. It must not be too wasteful and you will need to consider how well it will look displayed in sports shops, how it will pack into boxes for delivery and how strong it is. Design and make different packs and then decide which one you will put forward as your suggestion.

1. Design as many different shapes of box as possible. Make them in sugar paper, and when you're sure they are right, in card. Decorate them and display the selection.
2. Look at how they fasten together. With flaps? With tabs fitting into slots? Do they need glue? Look at plaited shapes.

3. Make a list of the advantages and disadvantages of each box. Choose one to look at more closely.
4. Make a template of its net. The card comes in rolls which are 64 cm wide. Arrange several of your nets onto card and try to waste as little card as possible. How long is your pattern? (i.e. how big a cutting design would have to be made?) What percentage of the card will be wasted? Show what method you used to find the area of the templates/left over card.
5. If a roll of card 100 m long cost ... then how much would each box cost (in terms of card)?
6. Now make up several boxes of the same design. Do they fit together without leaving spaces? What shape boxes would they best pack into? How many would you be able to get into a packing box? How many would you be able to get into a delivery truck, which measures 2 m × 2.5 m × 4 m?'

VARIATIONS

1. 'Look at the nets of flattened boxes. Can you tell what shape each one was when it was a box? What do you think it might have contained?'
2. Do other design projects – a box for an Easter egg or a pop-up birthday card.

Graphic Calculator Activities

NAT 1
2 3 4 5

NAT 3
6 7 8 9

EQUIPMENT

Graphic calculators
Graph paper
Teacher's sheet and acetate (page 39)
Sheets of axes for pupils to record their tries (positive quadrant/all 4 quadrants).
Activities 1–7 (pages 40–45)
Hunt the Number Activities 1–5 (page 46)

INSTRUCTIONS

The following activities are designed for a Casio fx-7000 G Graphics Calculator.

For Activity 3 photocopy the teacher's sheet onto acetate and then cut up into 25 puzzle sheets to hand out.

It is important for the pupils to record what they have found out. You could either draw up some sheets of axes (2 and 4 quadrants) for them to draw their graphs on, or they could use squared paper or graph paper.

Graphic Calculator Activities Teacher's sheet

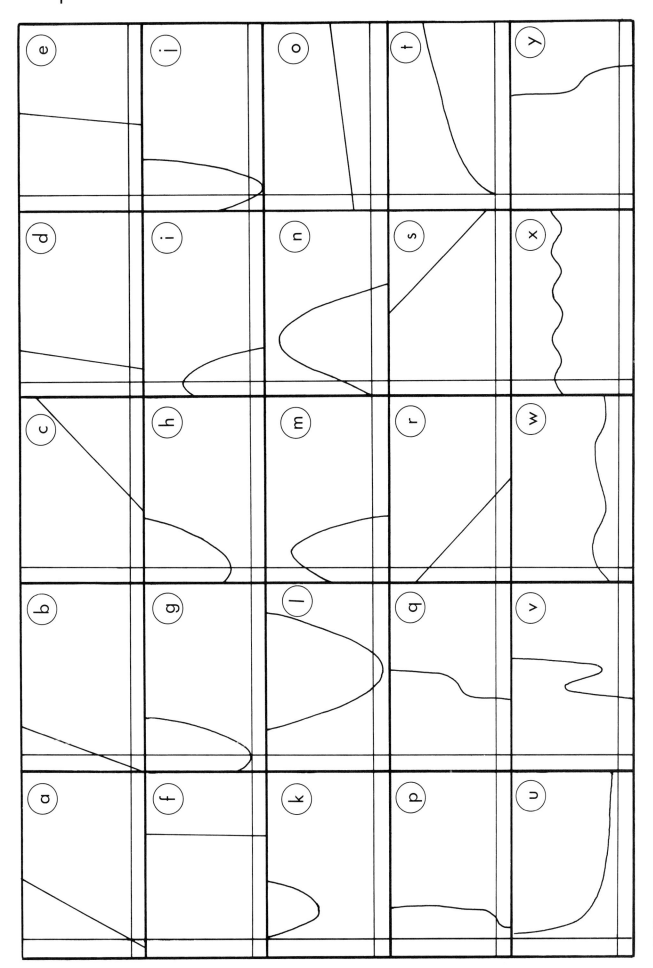

ACTIVITY ONE

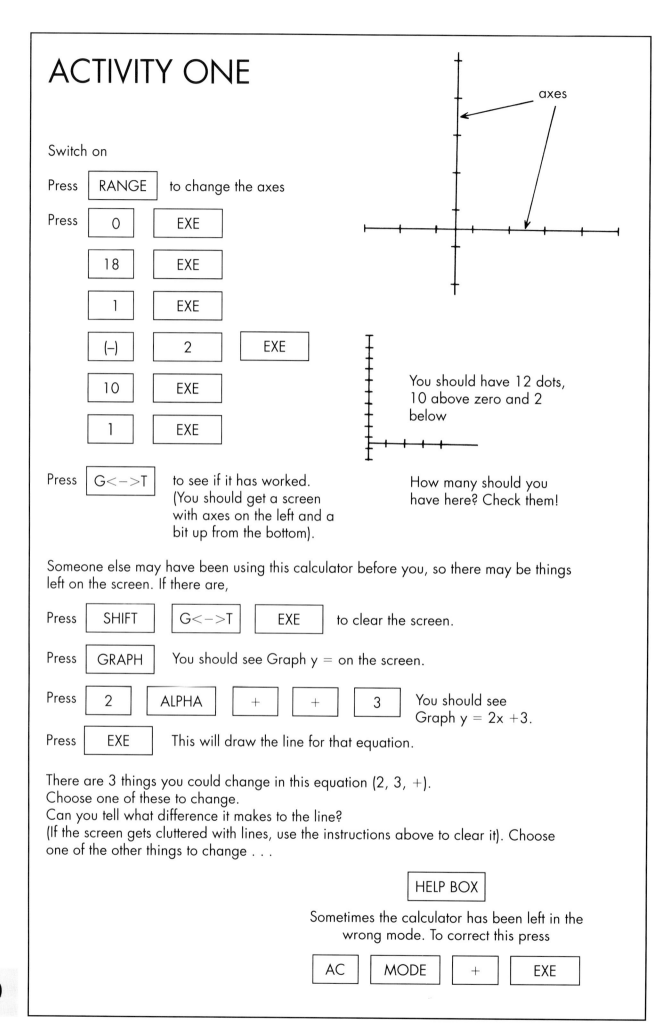

Switch on

Press | RANGE | to change the axes

Press | 0 | EXE |

| 18 | EXE |

| 1 | EXE |

| (–) | 2 | EXE |

| 10 | EXE |

| 1 | EXE |

axes

You should have 12 dots, 10 above zero and 2 below

Press | G<–>T | to see if it has worked. (You should get a screen with axes on the left and a bit up from the bottom).

How many should you have here? Check them!

Someone else may have been using this calculator before you, so there may be things left on the screen. If there are,

Press | SHIFT | G<–>T | EXE | to clear the screen.

Press | GRAPH | You should see Graph y = on the screen.

Press | 2 | ALPHA | + | + | 3 | You should see Graph y = 2x +3.

Press | EXE | This will draw the line for that equation.

There are 3 things you could change in this equation (2, 3, +).
Choose one of these to change.
Can you tell what difference it makes to the line?
(If the screen gets cluttered with lines, use the instructions above to clear it). Choose one of the other things to change . . .

| HELP BOX |

Sometimes the calculator has been left in the wrong mode. To correct this press

| AC | MODE | + | EXE |

40

ACTIVITY TWO

Set your [RANGE]   x min   0   (Press [EXE] each time to move down
                              max   12   to the next line).
                              scl   1
                              y min -2
                              max   6
                              scl   1

Press [G<–>T] to check if it has worked.
Clear screen if necessary.

Press Plot (This is [SHIFT] [MDISP])

Press [5] [SHIFT] [( ] [3] [EXE]   You should see a
                                                point flashing.

Put in any equation. (Use [GRAPH]).

Did it go through your point?

If not, press [GRAPH] and try again!

When you find an equation which goes through your point, write it down
somewhere.
Clear the screen.
Plot (5, 3) again as before.

Press [GRAPH] again and try to find a *different* equation which *also* has a line
                        going through this point.

How many can you find?
Make a list of the ones which DID go through the point.
Look at some of the ones which DIDN'T.
Can you find out why some worked and others didn't.

Clear the screen.
Choose another point to plot.
Try to find equations whose lines go through this new point.
Or give the calculator with the new point plotted to someone else and ask *them* to find
lines which go through it.

(You might like to go back and change the range so that you can look at points like
(15, 27).

ACTIVITY THREE

Hunt the Equation!

These clear sheets have each had the line of an equation drawn on.

Set the RANGE first.

Set it to (−)1, 23, 1, (−)2, 14, 1.

Choose one of the sheets to try.   (Remember to clear the screen you use)

To put an equation in press | GRAPH | | SHIFT | | G<−>T | | EXE |

When you think you have found an equation which fits the line on your sheet, record the number of the sheet and your equation.

Choose another sheet.

Now choose a sheet which has a *curved* line!

Have you found any equations which produce curves yet?

If not, you may need to ask your teacher for a hint!

Find an equation to fit the curve on your sheet.

Record your answer.

Choose another curve sheet . . .

ACTIVITY FOUR

A Challenge!

Set RANGE to (−)12, 12, 1, (−)8, 8, 1.

Now you have found some equations which produce curves, can you find one which makes a curve which will fit exactly into the top right hand quarter of the screen? Like this

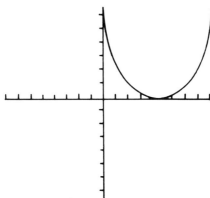

ACTIVITY FIVE

Set your range to   x min   0
                       max 10
                       scl   1
                    y min   −6
                       max 24
                       scl   1

Now try to draw 3 lines on the screen to form the biggest triangle possible. (Use GRAPH).

When you have found a really big triangle write down the 3 equations you used to make it.

Are they the same as anyone else's? You may need to work out the area of your triangle to see if it is bigger than the triangles other people have drawn.

Did your triangle have a horizontal line? If so, you could now try to draw the biggest triangle you can *without* a horizontal line . . . !

Change the range to x min −12
                        max 12
                        scl   1
                     y min   -8
                        max   8
                        scl   1

Try to draw the biggest possible triangle on *this* screen.

You can make this a new challenge as many times as you like by changing the range.

Can you start to *predict* which equations might produce useful lines on different screens?

ACTIVITY SIX

Set your range to   x   min   0
                          max 18
                          scl   1
                  y   min   −2
                          max 10
                          scl   1

Draw a square of any size. (Use GRAPH).

Write down the 4 equations you used. Comments?

Can you *predict* four more equations which would work?

Try them.

Another 4?

Change the range to x   min   0
                          max 20
                          scl   1
                  y min   −4
                          max 30
                          scl   2

Try your 4 equations again. Do you still get a square?

Find 4 equations which will work on this new screen.

You can make this problem a new challenge as often as you like by changing the range.

Can you draw a square which is in the third quadrant?
(The bottom left hand quarter). Use a range which shows it!
(e.g. −12, 2, 1, −8, 2, 1).

For a different challenge, see who can draw the biggest quadrilateral.

Now see if you can draw a vertical line.

ACTIVITY SEVEN

Here are 4 equations: $y = x^2$ $y = 2x^2$ $y = 3x^2 - 2x$ $y = 5x^2 - 4x + 9$

Which of these graphs goes with which equation?

Try to work it out before you check with your calculator.

Write down how you decided.

Were you correct?

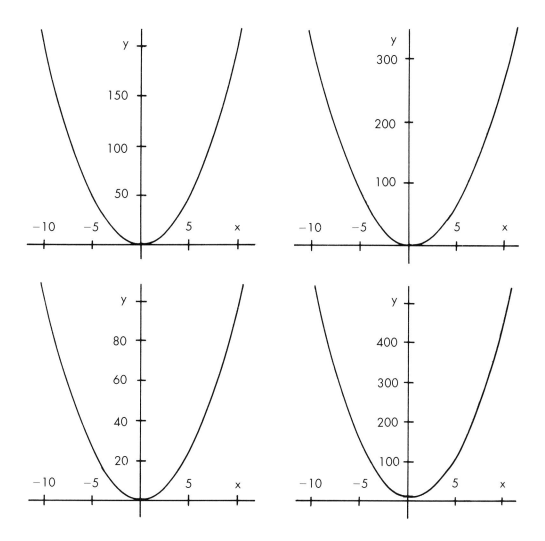

Write down 4 equations of your own.

Use your calculator to check the graphs which they produce.

Draw the 4 graphs carefully.

Give them to someone else as a puzzle like this one.

Try equations with different powers.

For each of the following Hunt the number activities first work out what my number was. Then make up a puzzle of your own for somebody else to solve.

Hunt the number (1)

I chose a number below 1000.

I used the square root button.

So I put in | $\sqrt{}$ | | my number | The answer was 25.65151068.

Hunt the number (2)

I chose a number below 1000.

I found the cube root of it.

I used | 3 | | $\sqrt[x]{}$ | | my number | The answer was 9.442870428.

Hunt the number (3)

I chose a number below 100.

I found out what it was as a logarithm.

I put in | log | | my number | The answer was 1.785329835.

Hunt the number (4)

I chose a number below 50.

I found out the sine of the number.

I put in | sin | | my number | The answer was 0.629320391.

Hunt the number (5)

I chose a number below 50.

I found out the cosine of the number.

I put in | cos | | my number | The answer was 0.8480480962.

Can you find any other buttons to use?

Harvest Supper

NAT 1	NAT 3
2 3 4	2 3 4 5 6

EQUIPMENT

Squared paper
Square tiles (*optional*)

INSTRUCTIONS

'Arthur always gets the hall ready for the harvest supper. The tables are square and a bit rickety so that they don't stand very well on their own. They have hooks on the sides so that you can fasten them together. Arthur always connects them all together so that they are firm. Each side of a table is big enough to seat one person. He always tries to put out exactly the right number of places.

This year he is told there are 38 people coming. Can you make an arrangement of the tables which seats 38? How many tables did you need? What is the least number of tables needed to seat 38? What is the most number of tables needed to seat 38? How can you be sure you've found the most and the least?

One more person buys a ticket. Can you make a table arrangement to seat 39?'

VARIATIONS

1. 'The vicar wants to clean out the storeroom and tells Arthur he must put *all* the tables out. There are 40. The hall will only hold 15 tables lengthwise and 10 tables across. What's the largest number of people they could seat, and what's the smallest number (with no spare places).
2. For 4 tables the most you can seat is 10 and the least is 8. What about 5, 6, 7 etc?'

The Idiot Rubic Cube Factory

NAT 1	NAT 2	NAT 3
2 3 4 5	3 4	2 3 4 5

EQUIPMENT

A $3 \times 3 \times 3$ cube made of black multilink cubes, and with a white sticker on all 54 circles
Multilink cubes and multiprisms
Isometric paper

INSTRUCTIONS

Use any variation of the story to introduce the problem.

'Once upon a time a group of idiots got together to run a factory making rubic cubes. The factory ran well but there was a problem. Nobody wanted to buy their rubic cubes. The reasons for this would have been obvious to anyone except an idiot – *all* the sides were the same colour, and, another small drawback; they wouldn't twist.

The marketing-idiot sold a few to friends of idiots and one or two interior decorators bought them to put on coffee tables for bored guests to talk about. Apart from that they just accumulated in the warehouse. The managing-idiot called a meeting. Something had to be done. The advertising-idiot had a brain-wave. "We must make them bigger – people aren't buying them because they're too small. Let's make a $10 \times 10 \times 10$ cube!! People will flock to buy them!"

"We'll need a lot more little cubes" cried the supervisor-idiot, "I'll organize the working-idiots into departments, Department 1 will make cubes with no spots, Dept. 2 will make cubes with 1 spot, Dept. 3 – 2 spots, Dept. 4 – 3 spots, Dept. 5 – 4 spots, Dept. 6 – 5 spots and Dept. 7 will make cubes with 6 spots!"

'If you were a lazy working-idiot which department would you go and work for?

If you were a working-idiot with a big mortgage and wanted lots of overtime, which department would you go and work for?

When the 10 cube doesn't sell either, the director-idiot tells them to make 15 cubes and 20 cubes. How many little cubes of each sort will be needed for each one of these?'

VARIATIONS

The Rubic Cross
The Rubic Prism

Kite

NAT 1	NAT 2	NAT 4
2 3 4	3 4	4 5

EQUIPMENT

Thin pieces of wood
Thin material or paper
String
Glue
Scissors
Sellotape
Ruler
Staple gun
Paper
Pencil

INSTRUCTIONS

1. 'Design a kite (box or ordinary).
2. Draw it in detail with measurements and clear instructions how to make it.
3. Build it.
4. Test it.
5. Alter it until you get the best flier.
6. What effect does the length of the tail have?
7. Or the angle at which the strings join?'

VARIATIONS

Have a competition to see which group can build the most successful kite.

Millions

EQUIPMENT

Paper
Pencil
Worksheet 7 (page 84)
Reference book(s) on large
   numbers
Calculator

INSTRUCTIONS

'A million has 6 zeros. What do we call this number: 1,000,000,000? Or this one: 10,000,000,000,000?! Find out about the names of numbers with lots of zeros. Do Americans use the same system?
   Try the questions on the worksheet.
   Make up some "millions" questions of your own to give to your friends to answer.'

VARIATIONS

1. 'Can you find out the volume of the earth? And the world population (to the nearest million). If we could share the earth out equally, how much would each person have?
2. Can you find out the area of the British Isles? And its population (to the nearest million). If all the people who live in the British Isles had to have the same amount of land to live on, how much would they each have?
3. Do the same for other countries. Compare how much room a British person would have with an American or someone from Singapore.'

Millions Answers
1. 1,000,000 seconds = 16666.6^r minutes = 277.7^r hours = 11.574 days.
2. 1,000,000 minutes = 16666.6^r hours = 694.4^r days = 1.9 years.
3. 1,000,000 hours = 41666.6^r days = 114 years.
4. 1,000,000 days = 2,737.85 years
$$\frac{1,991}{4,728}$$

5.6. 1,000,000 ounces = 62500 lbs = 4464.285 stones = 558.035 cwt.
   $= 27.9$ tons.
7. 1,000,000p = £10,000.

8. 1,000,000 inches = 83333.3^r feet = 27777.7^r yards = 15.78 miles.
9. 1,000,000 feet = 333333.3^r yards = 189.39 miles.
10. 1,000,000 yards = 568.18 miles.

11. Average page = 10 × 38
   1,000,000 words = 2631.579 pages = 10.5 books.
   Average number of pages = 250.

12. 1,000,000 inch^2 = 6944.4^r ft^2 = 771 yd^2.
13. 1,000,000 ft^2 = 111111.1^r yd^2 = 22.95 acres ($\div$ 4840).
14. 17,000,000 ft = 5666666.6^r yds = 3,219.69 miles.

Negative Colouring

NAT 1	NAT 3	NAT 4
2 3 4	2 3 4	3 4 5

EQUIPMENT

Squared paper
Black pen or pencil

INSTRUCTIONS

'Take one square. Decide how you're going to colour it in.

Use that square as the top left hand quarter of a new square. Colour in the three new squares the *opposite* way round (black area becomes white and white area becomes black).

Use this new square as the top left hand quarter of an even bigger square and again colour the others in the negative etc.

Do any patterns emerge?
Is there any symmetry within the pattern?
Can you predict whether a certain area will be black or white?

VARIATIONS

Do on the floor with reversible tiles.
Use a blank wall.
Use isometric paper with triangles or hexagons.

Nine Circles

NAT 1	NAT 2	NAT 3
2 3 4	2 3	4

EQUIPMENT

Paper
Pencil
Calculator (*optional*)

INSTRUCTIONS

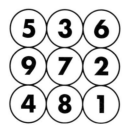

'Add the three horizontal numbers. Subtract the three vertical numbers. e.g.
$536 + 972 + 481 - 594 - 378 - 621 = 396$
   Can you make a larger answer by rearranging the numbers?
   Or a smaller one? Who has the largest? Smallest?
   How many possible totals *are* there?'
   This can be done as a group activity, pooling results.

VARIATIONS

1. Use multiplication and division. (On a 2 × 2 pattern i.e. 4 circles). Useful for comparing sizes with decimals, rounding up, significant figures.
2. Use a different rule about what you add – e.g. use the diagonals.
3. Make up a different shape, e.g.

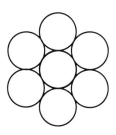

Number Wheels

NAT 1	NAT 2
2 3 4	2 3

EQUIPMENT

Compass
Ruler
Pencil
Paper
Counters/paper circles with the numbers on
Worksheets 8–10 (pages 85–87)

INSTRUCTIONS

Hand out Worksheet 8.
'Here are two hexagonal number wheels. In the first one can you place the numbers 1–13 in the circles so that every three circles joined by a straight line (six trios round the edge and three going across the wheel) add up to the same total? Is there more than one way to do it?

In the second one you have to use the numbers 1–19. The trios which must have the same totals are the six around the edge and the six spokes of the wheel. Try making each trio add up to 23. Then try totalling to 22. Can you find different ways of doing it?

Can you explain how you solved them?'

VARIATIONS

1. Hand out Worksheet 9.
   'Would square wheels work!? Using the numbers 1–9.
2. Hand out Worksheet 10.
   'Would octagons work? Using the numbers 1–17 on Octagon 4, or the numbers 1–25 on Octagon 5.'

REFERENCES

Starting idea from *Mathematical Amusement Arcade*, Brian Bolt p. 53, Cambridge University Press, 1984.

Palindromes

EQUIPMENT

Paper
Pen
Calculator (*optional*)
Number Grid
Computer (*optional*)
Examples of palindromes in English e.g. Warts to go, so got straw
Was it a car or a cat I saw

INSTRUCTIONS

'Choose any number, reverse the digits and add the two numbers.

E.g.
$$216$$
$$+ 612$$

Palindromic ⟶ 828

Try another:
$$154$$
$$+ 451$$

605 ⟵ Not palindromic so repeat process
$$+ 506$$

1111 ⟵ Palindromic

Does this always happen?
How many reversals before it does?'
    The cheat sheets for teachers give my results up to 799.

VARIATIONS

1. 'Look for palindromic numbers around you: telephone numbers, house numbers, dates. Which years produce most palindromic dates? Who can find two dates very close to each other which are both palindromes? (written 7.8.87 etc.)

2. Choose 3 digits (2, 3, 5). Make all possible 2-digit numbers with them (23, 32, 25, 52, 53, 35) Add them up (220) Add your first 3 digits (10) Divide your big total by your smaller one (22). The answer is a palindrome – why? Try it with 4 digits or 3 2-digit numbers.

REFERENCES

A program in Basic for the BBC computer for producing palindromes can be found on p.79 of *Mathematics for Low Attainers* by Biddle, Savage, Smith and Vowles, published by West Sussex Institute of Higher Education, 1985.

No.	St.	Ans.	No.	St.	Ans.	No.	St.	Ans.	No.	St.	Ans.
10	1	11	74	1	121	139	2	1771	204	1	606
12	1	33	75	2	363	140	1	181	205	1	707
13	1	44	76	2	484	142	1	383	206	1	808
14	1	55	78	4	4884	143	1	484	207	1	909
15	1	66	79	6	44044	144	1	585	208	2	1111
16	1	77	80	1	88	145	1	686	209	1	1111
17	1	88	81	1	99	146	1	787	210	1	222
18	1	99	82	2	121	147	1	888	211	1	323
19	2	121	83	1	121	148	1	989	213	1	525
20	1	22	84	2	363	149	2	1991	214	1	626
21	1	33	85	2	484	150	2	303	215	1	127
23	1	55	86	3	1111	152	2	707	216	1	828
24	1	66	87	4	4884	153	2	909	217	1	929
25	1	77	89	24	8813200023188	154	2	1111	218	2	1331
26	1	88	90	1	99	155	3	4444	219	2	2442
27	1	99	91	2	121	156	3	6666	220	1	242
28	2	121	92	1	121	157	3	8888	221	1	343
29	1	121	93	2	363	158	3	11011	223	1	545
30	1	33	94	2	484	159	2	1221	224	1	646
31	1	44	95	3	1111	160	2	343	225	1	747
32	1	55	96	4	4884	162	2	747	226	1	848
34	1	77	97	6	44044	163	2	949	227	1	949
35	1	88	98	24	8813200023188	164	3	2662	228	2	1551
36	1	99	100	1	101	165	3	4884	229	2	2662
37	2	121	102	1	303	166	5	45254	230	1	262
38	1	121	103	1	404	167	11	88555588	231	1	363
39	2	363	104	1	505	168	3	13431	233	1	565
40	1	44	105	1	606	169	2	1441	234	1	666
41	1	55	106	1	707	170	2	383	235	1	767
42	1	66	107	1	808	172	2	787	236	1	868
43	1	77	108	1	909	173	2	989	237	1	969
45	1	99	109	2	1111	174	4	5115	238	2	1771
46	2	121	110	1	121	175	4	9559	239	2	2882
47	1	121	112	1	323	176	5	44044	240	1	282
48	2	363	113	1	424	177	15	8836886388	241	1	383
49	2	484	114	1	525	178	6	15851	242	0	242
50	1	55	115	1	626	179	2	1661	243	1	585
51	1	66	116	1	727	180	2	747	244	1	686
52	1	77	117	1	828	182	6	45254	245	1	787
53	1	88	118	1	929	183	4	13431	246	1	888
54	1	99	119	2	1331	184	3	2552	247	1	989
56	1	121	120	1	141	185	3	4774	248	2	1991
57	2	363	122	1	343	186	3	6996	249	3	5115
58	2	484	123	1	444	187	23	8813200023188	250	2	505
59	3	1111	124	1	545	188	7	233332	251	2	707
60	1	66	125	1	646	189	2	1881	253	2	1111
61	1	77	126	1	747	190	7	45254	254	3	4444
62	1	88	127	1	848	192	4	6996	255	3	6666
63	1	99	128	1	949	193	8	233332	256	3	8888
64	2	121	129	2	1551	194	3	2992	257	3	11011
65	1	121	130	1	161	195	4	9339	258	2	1221
67	2	484	132	1	363	196			259	2	2332
68	3	1111	133	1	464	197	7	881188	260	2	545
69	4	4884	134	1	565	198	5	79497	261	2	747
70	1	77	135	1	666	199	3	3113	263	3	2662
71	1	88	136	1	767	200	1	202	264	3	4884
72	1	99	137	1	868	201	1	303	265	5	45254
73	2	121	138	1	969	203	1	505	266	11	88555588

53

No.	St.	Ans.	No.	St.	Ans.	No.	St.	Ans.	No.	St.	Ans.
267	3	13431	334	1	767	400	1	404	467	2	2552
268	2	1441	335	1	868	401	1	505	468	2	3663
269	2	1551	336	1	969	402	1	606	469	2	4774
270	2	585	337	2	1771	403	1	707	470	2	989
271	2	787	338	2	2882	405	1	909	471	4	5115
273	4	5115	339	2	3993	406	2	1111	472	4	9559
274	4	9559	340	1	383	407	1	1111	473	5	44044
275	5	44044	341	1	484	408	2	3333	475	3	15851
276			342	1	585	409	2	4444	476	2	1661
277	3	15851	344	1	787	410	1	424	477	2	2772
278	2	1661	345	1	888	411	1	525	478	2	3883
279	2	2772	346	1	989	412	1	626	479	2	4994
280	4	2662	347	2	1991	413	1	727	480	4	13431
281	6	45254	348	3	5115	415	1	929	481	3	2552
283	3	2552	349	3	7337	416	2	1331	482	3	4774
284	3	4774	350	2	707	417	2	2442	483	3	6996
285	3	6996	351	2	909	418	2	3553	485	7	233332
286	23	8813200023188	352	2	1111	419	2	4664	486	2	1881
287	7	233332	354	3	6666	420	1	444	487	2	2992
288	2	1881	355	3	8888	421	1	545	488	3	7117
289	2	2992	356	3	11011	422	1	646	489	3	9339
290	4	2552	357	2	1221	423	1	747	490	8	233332
291	4	6996	358	2	2332	425	1	949	491	3	2992
293	3	2992	359	2	3443	426	2	1551	492	4	9339
294	4	9339	360	2	747	427	2	2662	493		
295			361	2	949	428	2	3773	495	5	79497
296	7	881188	362	3	2662	429	2	4884	496	3	3113
297	5	79497	364	5	45254	430	1	464	497	3	5335
298	3	3113	365	11	88555588	431	1	565	498	3	7557
299	3	5335	366	3	13431	432	1	666	499	3	9779
300	1	303	367	2	1441	433	1	767	500	1	505
301	1	404	368	2	2552	435	1	969	501	1	606
302	1	505	369	2	3663	436	2	1771	502	1	707
304	1	707	370	2	787	437	2	2882	503	1	808
305	1	808	371	2	989	438	2	3993	504	1	909
306	1	909	372	4	5115	439	3	9119	506	1	1111
307	2	1111	374	5	44044	440	1	484	507	2	3333
308	1	1111	375	15	8836886388	441	1	585	508	2	4444
309	2	3333	376	3	15851	442	1	686	509	2	5555
310	1	323	377	2	1661	443	1	787	510	1	525
311	1	424	378	2	2772	445	1	989	511	1	626
312	1	525	379	2	3883	446	2	1991	512	1	727
314	1	727	380	6	45254	447	3	5115	513	1	828
315	1	828	381	4	13431	448	3	7337	514	1	929
316	1	929	382	3	2552	449	3	9559	516	2	2442
317	2	1331	384	3	6996	450	2	909	517	2	3553
318	2	2442	385	23	8813200023188	451	2	1111	518	2	4664
319	2	3553	386	7	233332	452	3	4444	519	2	5775
320	1	343	387	2	1881	453	3	6666	520	1	545
321	1	444	388	2	2992	455	3	11011	521	1	646
322	1	545	389	3	7117	456	2	1221	522	1	747
324	1	747	390	4	6996	457	2	2332	523	1	848
325	1	848	391	8	233332	458	2	3443	524	1	949
326	1	949	392	3	2992	459	2	4554	526	2	2662
327	2	1551	394			460	2	949	527	2	3773
328	2	2662	395	7	881188	461	3	2662	528	2	4884
329	2	3773	396	5	79497	462	3	4884	529	2	5995
330	1	363	397	3	3113	463	5	45254	530	1	565
331	1	464	398	3	5335	465	3	13431	531	1	666
332	1	565	399	3	7557	466	2	1441	532	1	767

54

No.	St.	Ans.	No.	St.	Ans.	No.	St.	Ans.	No.	St.	Ans.
533	1	868	600	1	606	667	2	4774	733	2	1771
534	1	969	601	1	707	668	2	5885	734	2	2882
536	2	2882	602	1	808	669	2	6996	735	2	3993
537	2	3993	603	1	909	670	4	9559	736	3	9119
538	3	9119	604	2	1111	671	5	44044	738	5	99099
539	4	25652	605	1	1111	672	15	8836886388	739		
540	1	585	607	2	4444	673	3	15851	740	1	787
541	1	686	608	2	5555	674	2	1661	741	1	888
542	1	787	609	2	6666	675	2	2772	742	1	989
543	1	888	610	1	626	677	3	9339	743	2	1991
544	1	989	611	1	727	678	3	9449	744	3	5115
546	3	5115	612	1	828	679	4	47674	745	3	7337
547	3	7337	613	1	929	680	3	4774	746	3	9559
548	3	9559	614	2	1331	681	3	6996	748	4	44044
549	5	59895	615	2	2442	682	23	8813200023188	749	4	68486
550	2	1111	617	2	4664	683	7	471174	750	3	6666
551	3	4444	618	2	5775	684	2	1881	751	3	8888
552	3	6666	619	2	6886	685	4	6556	752	3	11011
553	3	8888	620	1	646	687	3	9339	753	2	1221
554	3	11011	621	1	747	688	8	1136311	754	2	2332
556	2	2332	622	1	848	689			755	2	3443
557	2	3443	623	1	949	690	4	9339	756	2	4554
558	2	4554	624	2	1551	691			758	2	6776
559	2	5665	625	2	2662	692	7	881188	759	2	7887
560	3	2662	627	2	4884	693	5	22022	760	5	45254
561	3	4884	628	2	5995	694	3	3113	761	11	88555588
562	5	45254	629	4	45254	695	3	5335	762	3	13431
563	11	88555588	630	1	666	697	3	9779	763	2	1441
564	3	13431	631	1	767	698	4	22022	764	2	2552
566	2	2552	632	1	868	699	4	46464	765	2	3663
567	2	3663	633	1	969	700	1	707	766	2	4774
568	2	4774	634	2	1771	701	1	808	768	2	6996
569	2	5885	635	2	2882	702	1	909	769	4	67276
570	4	5115	637	3	9119	703	2	1111	770	5	44044
571	4	9559	638	4	25652	704	1	1111	771	15	8836886388
572	5	44044	639	5	99099	705	2	3333	772	3	15851
573	15	8836886388	640	1	686	706	2	4444	773	2	1661
574	3	15851	641	1	787	708	2	6666	774	2	2772
576	2	2772	642	1	888	709	2	7777	775	2	3883
577	2	3883	643	1	989	710	1	727	776	2	4994
578	2	4994	644	2	1991	711	1	828	778	4	47674
579	4	23232	645	3	5115	712	1	929	779	6	475574
580	3	2552	647	3	9559	713	2	1331	780	3	6996
581	3	4774	648	2	59895	714	2	2442	781	23	8813200023188
582	3	6996	649	4	44044	715	2	3553	782	7	233332
583	23	8813200023188	650	2	4444	716	2	4664	783	2	1881
584	7	233332	651	3	6666	718	2	6886	784	2	2992
586	2	2992	652	3	8888	719	2	7997	785	3	7117
587	3	7117	653	3	11011	720	1	747	786	3	9339
588	3	93339	654	2	1221	721	1	848	788		
589	8	1136311	655	2	2332	722	1	949	789	4	66066
590	3	2992	657	2	4554	723	2	1551	790		
591	4	9339	658	2	5665	724	2	2662	791	7	881188
592			659	2	6776	725	2	3773	792	5	79497
593	7	881188	660	3	4884	726	2	4884	793	3	3113
594	5	79497	661	2	45254	728	4	45254	794	3	5335
596	3	5335	662	11	88555588	729	4	69696	795	3	7557
597	3	7557	663	3	13431	730	1	767	796	3	9779
598	3	9779	664	2	1441	731	1	868	798	4	46464
599	4	22022	665	2	2552	732	1	969	799	6	449944

The Perimeter is . . .

EQUIPMENT

Plain paper
Squared or dotted paper
Pencil
Or a pinboard and elastic bands
Or straws connected by pipe-cleaners (1 straw = 1 hurdle)

INSTRUCTIONS

1. 'A farmer has twenty sheep hurdles, each 1 metre long, with which to make a sheep pen. How many different shaped pens could he make if all the corners are right angles? Be careful to cross out any reflections or rotations.
   Investigate the pens possible with other lengths of fence.
2. He no longer keeps to right-angled corners. What difference does this make?
3. Instead of hurdles he goes and buys a roll of flexible fencing. What is the biggest area he can *now* enclose with 20 metres?'

VARIATIONS

In part 1:
(a) 'How many different *areas* do these pens have?
(b) Can you make cut-outs of your pens fit together like a jigsaw?'

In parts 2 and 3:
(a) 'He decides to build his pen next to a wall, so one side is already supplied by the wall. What is the biggest area he can now enclose with 20 metres of fence? How much of the wall does he use? Try other lengths of fencing.
(b) He has two walls which join at right angles to supply two sides of the pen . . . or two walls joined at 80°, 100°, 110° . . . .'

Pictures from Bearings

EQUIPMENT

Pencil
Ruler
Protractor
Worksheet 11 (page 88)

INSTRUCTIONS

Use the worksheet. The bearings for method 1 produce this shape.

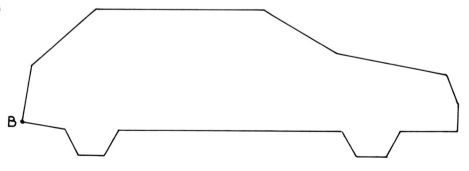

The bearings for method 2
produce this shape.

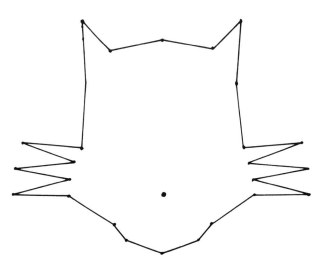

In this example the starting point was in the centre of the final shape, but pictures could be made up with start points outside the shape or even on the outline. Method 2 is simpler because there are no new North lines to draw in. Method 1 is more like the exam questions about planes flying so many km at 085° etc. but it has the advantage over exam-type questions that the pupils know it should come out as something recognizable and that the last bearing should close the shape.

Probability Mazes

NAT 1			NAT 5		
2	3	4	3	4	5

EQUIPMENT

Dice (various)
Squared paper
Isometric paper
Pencil
Worksheets 12–13 (pages 89–90)

INSTRUCTIONS

'Follow the rules for each maze. Do each one lots of times.
    Can you decide which is the most likely exit? And the least likely?
    Can you work out the probability of arriving at each exit?'

VARIATIONS

Change the rules.
Change the number or type of dice.
'Make up some mazes of your own on different types of paper.'

Reducing to Zero

NAT 1	NAT 2	NAT 3
2 3 4	2 3	3 4 5

EQUIPMENT

Paper
Pencil
Calculator

INSTRUCTIONS

'Pick any 4-digit number. Reduce it to zero in four steps by using add/subtract/multiply/divide and any 2-digit numbers.

e.g.: $1250 \div 25 - 30 - 10 - 10$

When you have done a few of these (stick to *whole* numbers) try reducing to zero using the four rules *once each*.

e.g.: $1250 \div 25 - 51 \times 37 + 37$

This example went negative. Can you do it *without* any stage being negative?

Try some more start numbers.'

VARIATIONS

1. 'Using *any* of the four rules with a 2-digit number, what is the least number of stages needed to reduce a 4-digit start number to zero. Or a 5-, 6-, 7-digit start number?
2. Use only single digits to do the reducing. Or more than 2 digits etc.'
3. Specify the order in which the four rules must be used. Are any orders impossible?
4. Make it six stages to include square and square root.

Round Bales

NAT 1	NAT 2	NAT 4
2 3 4	2 3 4	2 3 4 5 6

EQUIPMENT

Information about round and square bales from agricultural machinery salesman, (dimension, density, etc.) (page 59)

The 3 main bale sizes are:

Ht.		Width
4'	×	4'
5'	×	4'
6'	×	5'

Paper
Pencil

INSTRUCTIONS

'A farmer changes from square to round bales. He has a barn where he normally stores his straw and he has to work out how best to store it in these new round bales. Make up a reasonable size of barn and see how many he can get inside. Draw a diagram to show how they are arranged. How many square bales could he have got into the same barn? (Machinery can't cope with lifting round bales more than 4 feet high).

Then he buys some Rollatex to wrap the bales and make them weather-proof. They can now be stacked outside on their sides. He makes 84 round bales. Find a way of stacking them which won't take up too much room.'

VARIATIONS

Persuade a local farmer to deliver a round bale and a square bale to school so that you can actually find out the dimensions.

Get the class to use some of the other information about balers to make up questions for other people to answer (e.g. about bale weight: 'If a lorry used to be able to carry 200 square bales (in weight), how many round bales will it be able to carry?').

ROUND BALES

Bales measurements and weights for all models:

	85	62 S	44 S	34 S
Diameter m	1.80	1.60	1.20	0.90
Width m	1.50	1.22	1.22	1.20
Weight kg				
for hay	610	385	215	120
for straw	500	310	175	100
for silage	–	725	405	230

A Choice of Two Models

The RP12 and the RP15 are roll balers of similar design; the main difference between them is that they produce bales of different sizes. Both models have bale chambers 1.2m (4') wide, but the RP12 has a chamber diameter of 1.2m (4'), while the RP has a chamber diameter of 1.55m (5'2").

The baler uses 3000 m rolls of ROLLATEX net which is sufficient for approximately 300 bales, depending on the number of wraps.

The farmer can quickly change from harvesting hay to baling silage. Harvesting well-wilted forage with the roll baler has many advantages. Wilting to between 50% and 70% dry matter content is favourable for good fermentation, increases nutritional value and reduces bale weight and numbers. Baler performance of up to 2 hectares per hour are possible.

Bales are hauled by the tractor front loader or rear-mounted fork. If both are used together, the field is cleared in half the time, at a rate of up to 3 hectares per hour.

Philip's team wrapped 9000 bales, equivalent to 4500 tonnes of silage, and in the process used 6½ tonnes of wrapping film.

Bale weight (according to moisture content)	Straw:	120–180 kg
	Hay:	180–300 kg
	Semi-wilted hay:	450–600 kg

Tying material		
Sisal twine	runnage 200 or 300 m/kg	runnage 200 or 300 m/kg
Plastic twine	runnage 400–700 m/kg	runnage 400–700 m/kg
Twine consumption per 10 bales	approx. 600 m (at 12 wrappings)	approx. 900 m (at 15 wrappings)

SQUARE BALES

They set new standards for performance for pick-up balers with conventional size baling chamber (0.36 × 0.49 m).

Technical Data	AP630	AP400	AP500
Chamber size	36 × 49 cm	30 × 40 cm	36 × 48 cm
Bale length steplessly variable	0.50–1.20 m	0.50–1.20 m	0.50–1.20 m
Bale length depending on length and density	12–35 kg	8–20 kg	10–30 kg
Tying material			
Sisal twine	runnage 125–200 m/kg	runnage 125–200 m/kg	runnage 125–200 m/kg
Plastic twine	runnage 250–400 m/kg	runnage 250–400 m/kg	runnage 250–400 m/kg
Tying material consumption per 100 bales at medium bale length of 0.8 m	464 m	444 m	464 m
Twine box, holding capacity	14 rolls	4 rolls	4 rolls

Servicetill Cards

NAT 1	NAT 2	NAT 3
2 3 4 5	3 4	3 4 5 6

EQUIPMENT

Examples of instant money cards
Paper
Pencil

INSTRUCTIONS

'My Dad asked me about my servicetill card. "Wasn't it dangerous?" he wanted to know. "What would happen if someone stole it and tried to use it?"

"Don't worry! I've got a four-digit personal number that only I and the bank know. If I don't punch that number in first I don't get any money. The machine just eats my card!"

"But what if someone guessed your number?"

"They couldn't – there must be thousands of possible numbers and the machine only gives you three tries."

"Thousands?"

"Well . . . lots . . . ."

How many combination of four numbers are there?'

VARIATIONS

1. 'If someone looked over my shoulder and saw the last two digits I punched in, and then stole my card, what's the probability of him guessing my four-digit number correctly?
2. If the thief only saw the last digit?
3. If all the four digits of my number had to be *different* (e.g. 4244 is not allowed) would this make a difference to your answers?'

Sheep Dealer

NAT 1	NAT 3
2 3 4	2 3 4 5 6

EQUIPMENT

Pencil
Worksheet 14 (page 91)

INSTRUCTIONS

'A sheep dealer goes to various markets during the week buying sheep in one and selling at others when the price is better. In the meantime he keeps the sheep on his farm. He is convinced that someone is rustling some of his sheep during the night, not large numbers, just ones and twos. He moves the sheep pens right up to the house (he has a very understanding wife) and arranges the pens as you can see on the sheet.

However, even though there is a window facing each way so that he can see all the pens, he finds it difficult to count up how many sheep are in all the pens and work out if any are missing. A friend suggests that he arrange the sheep so that whichever window he looks out of he will see the same number of sheep – then he only has to remember one number. He decides to try this.

In the first picture he has arranged twelve sheep so that whichever window he looks out of he can see four sheep. Could he have put them so that he sees three from each window? How many different ways could he arrange the twelve sheep? Try different numbers. Are there any numbers of sheep he should avoid because they won't arrange so that he can see the same number from each window?'

VARIATIONS

'His wife's favourite number is 6. For her birthday he promises to arrange the sheep so that she can see six from each window. What's the minimum number of sheep he needs to have in the pens that day? And the maximum? His daughter's favourite number is 7 . . .'

Sign Writing

NAT 1	NAT 3	NAT 5
2 3 4	4 5	2 3 4

EQUIPMENT

Card
Felt pens or coloured pencils
Long tape measure

INSTRUCTIONS

'You are hoping to start up a business painting signs for people. You have to work out how large the lettering needs to be. Some friends want you to do a sign saying "Free Range Eggs for Sale". The road in front of their house runs straight for about 300 yards and cars travel between 40–50 m.p.h. along it. How long will the drivers have the sign in view?

Make some trial signs.

How far away can people with average eyesight read the signs?

How long does it take to read those five words?

What if your friends wanted you to add "Freshly laid. Only £1.50 per dozen"?

Decide on the best sign for this situation.'

VARIATIONS

1. 'Consider different distances. Can you make up a rule of thumb about the size of the lettering depending on the distance away?
2. Consider different times. Can you make up a rule of thumb about how many words people can read per second or per minute?
3. Look at different colour backgrounds and lettering. Make the same sign in different variations and see which is clearest. Does the best combination alter with the time of day/amount of sunshine?
4. You have a large sign outside your house (choose one). Something (the hedge/drooping branches?) covers up either the top of the words or the bottom of the words. The sign is important. Which would you rather got covered, the top or the bottom?

Does it depend on the type of writing?

Which style of writing is most legible with top or bottom obscured?

Leaves blow down in Autumn and stick on your sign, blotting out various letters. Which letters are most/least important?

How many can get blotted out before it becomes unreadable?'

(The alphabets on page 62 show which letters can be confused.)

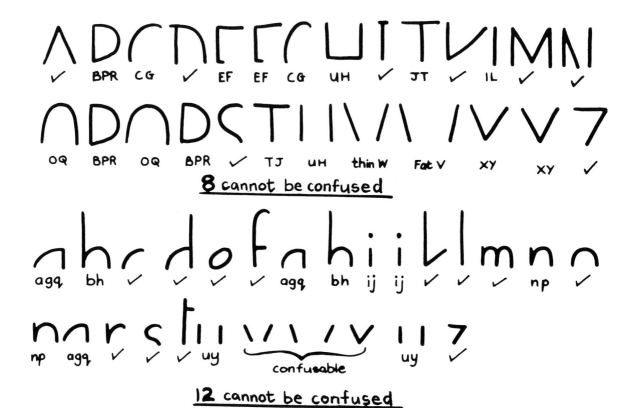

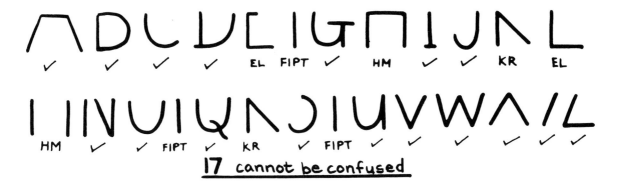

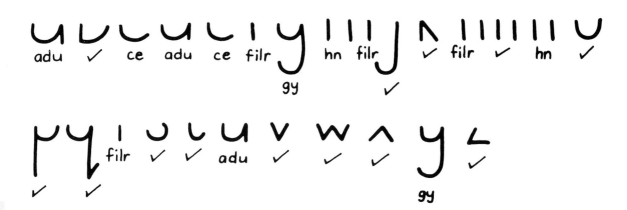

Skittles

EQUIPMENT

Paper
Pencil

INSTRUCTIONS

'In skittles each player plays 6 "hands" in an evening and the 6 scores are added up to give each player's total score for the game.

In my skittles league, if one of the players is ill we can still play the match with seven people. Where the eighth player should have been, we fill in scores which add up to 25. As a normal total score for a player in my team is 40 or over, the rest of the team have to play really well to win the game. If I were captain I might decide to boost my team's scores to give them confidence at the start. So I might put on the scoreboard:

	1	2	3	4	5	6	Player's total
Fran							
Joy							
Bet							
Extra	9	9	2	2	2	1	25
Team's Total							

Look at other variations.'

VARIATIONS

1. 'How many possibilities are there if you can have 0–25 in any square?
2. How many possibilities are there if you can write 0–9 in any square? (Over 9 is a spare, and your absent player is not allowed to score a spare!)
3. If you are not allowed zero (1–9).'

Splitting Thirteen

EQUIPMENT

Paper
Pencil

INSTRUCTIONS

'Split 13 in as many different ways as you can e.g. 10/3, 7/6, 12/1, 3/4/6, 2/2/2/2/2/3, 1/1/1/1/1/1/1/1/1/4, etc.

Multiply the split numbers together e.g. 10/3 = 30, 7/6 = 42, 12/1 = 12, 3/4/6 = 72, 2/2/2/2/2/3 = 96, etc.

Which split produces the highest product?

How many products are there?

How many products occur more than once? Why do they?'

VARIATIONS

1. Split other numbers.
2. Graph the results of a range of numbers and look for patterns.

Squares on a Chessboard

NAT 1	NAT 2	NAT 3	NAT 5
2 3 4 5	5	2 3 4 5 6	2 3 4

EQUIPMENT

Squared paper
Dotted paper
Pencil
Chessboard (*optional*)
Calculator (*for variations*)

INSTRUCTIONS

1. 'Find out how many squares there are (of all sizes) on a chessboard. (Start by finding the squares on a small board, and work up to it) e.g. on a 2 × 2 board there are 5 squares

		1	2
1	+	3	4

2. Could you now find the number of squares on a 20 × 20 square? Or a 100 × 100 square? How would you attempt it?*
3. Do the same investigation, but on dotted paper instead of squared which allows slanted squares to be counted too.
4. How about the rectangles on a chessboard!
5. Include parallelograms!!'

VARIATIONS

1. One grain of corn is put on a chessboard square, 2 grains on the next square, 3 on the third etc. How many grains are put on the board altogether? What about different sized boards?**
2. One grain of corn is put on the first square, 2 on the second, 4 on the third and so on doubling each time. How many would be put on the last square? How many altogether?***

   Formula for finding *sum of squares* =

   $$\frac{1}{6} n(n + 1)(2n + 1) \qquad n = \text{any number}$$

   **Formula* for finding sum of an *arithmetic progression* =

   $$Sn = \frac{n}{2} \{2a + (n - 1)d\}$$

   n = last number
   a = start number
   d = difference between each number

   ****Formula* for finding sum of a *geometric progression* =

   $$Sn = a\frac{(1 - r^n)}{1 - r}$$

   a = start number
   r = multiplier

Starting a Village Shop

NAT 1	NAT 2	NAT 5
2 3 4	2 3 4	2 3 4

EQUIPMENT

Brochures from Cash and Carry showing wholesale prices, recommended retail prices, percentage profits.
Calculator

INSTRUCTIONS

'You have bought a village shop. It has no stock in it. You have £4,000 left over to buy stock. Decide from the leaflets what you will buy and in what quantity. (Think about shelf-life.) Your weekly spending on mortgage, heating, lighting, food and petrol and insurance is £280. You must make enough money each week to pay the bills and replenish the stock.

Decide how you will price each item, what percentage profit this gives and then calculate your overall profit. In a good week you may sell over half your stock, but remember there will be bad weeks too.

How much of the stock do you need to sell to cover your costs?

How will you persuade people to use your shop?

Perhaps one item needs to be a loss leader?'

VARIATIONS

1. Write out a list of what you have in your shop. Give it to another group. Ask *them* to decide how many of each item is sold that week. Recalculate your profit on their sales.
2. Work out what a typical household spends and use that value instead of the £280. Could you economize on some items? Which and how?
3. Discuss whether £4,000 is a reasonable sum with which to stock a small shop. What items, which you might want to sell are not in the Cash and Carry brochures?

Survival Course

NAT 1   **NAT 3**
2 3 4 5 6   2 3 4 5 6

EQUIPMENT

Paper
Pencil
Openable link chain (*optional*), from the Jonathan Press Equipment Catalogue.
Survival Course sheet (page 66)

INSTRUCTIONS

'The Mathematical Marines sets its entrance task to test your mind as well as your muscle. Your only equipment is a length of chain and a number of hacksaw blades. Each link of the chain adds another inch to the chain's length. Each hacksaw blade will saw a hole in one link; then it self-destructs! You must have all possible connected chain lengths available, because at any time you may have to use an exact length of chain to survive. You will be set tasks which use all lengths of chain up to the maximum.

On the first day you are given one hacksaw blade. You can ask for the amount of chain you want. The first competitor is confident – he asks for 7 links, and uses the blade to cut it on the third link. Can he make all the connected chain lengths up to 7 inches? How much chain *should* he have asked for and where should he cut it?'

VARIATIONS

1. 'On day two of the course you are given two hacksaw blades. How much chain should you ask for and where will you make the two cuts?
2. On day three you are given three blades, etc.
3. What happens to this problem if the lengths of chain do not have to be connected i.e. for a chain 9 inches long you could use a 4 inch length and a 5 inch length without a connecting cut link?'

SURVIVAL COURSE

Why 7 links, cut on the third link won't work:

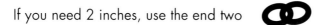

Cut here

If you need 1 inch, use the cut link

If you need 2 inches, use the end two

If you need 3 inches, use the end two and the cut link

If you need 4 inches, use the end four

If you need 5 inches, use the end four and the cut link

If you need 6 inches, . . . ?

If you need 7 inches, use the whole chain.

8 links to stop a poisoned
trap from closing

17 links to keep the
dogs shut away

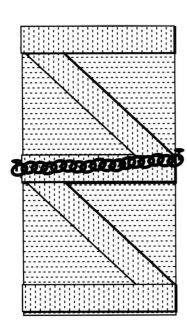

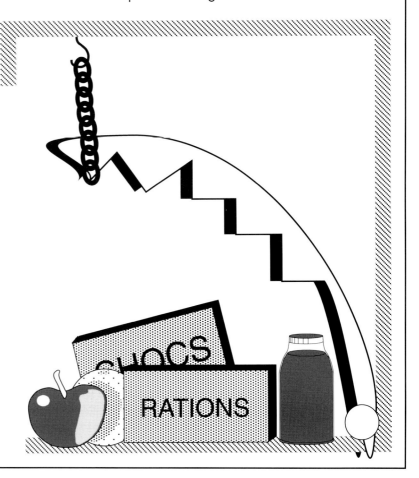

Symmetrical Shapes

EQUIPMENT

Scissors
Card
Pencil
Squared paper/isometric paper
Multilink cubes
Felt pens or coloured pencils

INSTRUCTIONS

'Choose three simple shapes based on joined squares and cut them out in card. Colour them in different colours. (The different colours are just to make recording easier.)

Here are three you could use.

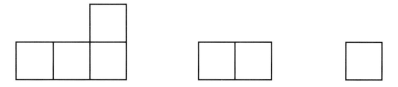

How many symmetrical shapes can you make using all three of your shapes, ignoring the colours? Record them as you find them. Make sure you draw in the line of symmetry.

When you are sure you have found all the possibilities, explain *why* you are sure.

Choose three more shapes and do the same. Or choose two or four or five shapes. Use seven unconnected squares. How many symmetrical shapes can you make?'

VARIATIONS

1. 'Make three solid shapes with multilink cubes. Make each one in a different colour. Here are three possibilities:

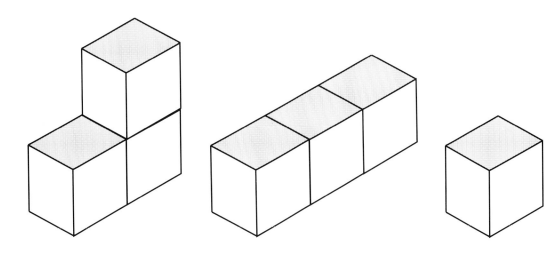

How many ways can you fit them together to make a solid with plane symmetry? Rotational symmetry? Draw them on isometric paper and show where the plane or axis of symmetry would be. Explain why, when you're sure you've found them all.

2. Use seven cubes to make all the possible symmetrical solids. Try other numbers of cubes.'

Target

EQUIPMENT

Large sheet of squared paper
Pack of 48 vector cards
2 counters labelled 'start' and 'target'
Pencil
Paper

INSTRUCTIONS

A game for 2–4 players.
'Decide which way up to have the sheet of paper and mark the sides (top, bottom, left, right) to avoid argument later!

Decide on a 'start' position and a 'target' position.

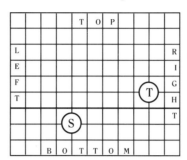

A correct combination for this board would be

$$\begin{pmatrix} 1 \\ 3 \end{pmatrix} \begin{pmatrix} 2 \\ 2 \end{pmatrix} \begin{pmatrix} 4 \\ 1 \end{pmatrix} \begin{pmatrix} -2 \\ -4 \end{pmatrix}$$

Deal out 10 cards each. Put the rest of the pack face down. Players take turns to make combinations of vector cards which will move them from start to target. Player 1 writes down his or her combination. The other player(s) checks to make sure it will work. If it works player 2 has a go and writes down a combination from his or her cards and so on.

The winner is the one who can still go when everyone else has run out of routes. Before starting a new game move the start and target counters to fresh positions.'

VARIATIONS

1. 'Move the 'target' after *each* go, by picking up the top card of the pack and moving accordingly.
2. Award points for the number of vector cards used. So if you made the journey from 'start' to 'target' using 3 vector cards you score 3 but if you used 7 vector cards, score 7.
3. Can you decide on 6 vectors (which you can use as many times as you like) to land on every intersection of a 6 × 6 board? Is it possible? Do you need more? Can you do it with less?

How many moves does it take? What if any card with a zero is disallowed? Smaller/larger boards?'

THE 48 VECTOR CARDS

$$\begin{pmatrix} 2 \\ -2 \end{pmatrix} \begin{pmatrix} -2 \\ 2 \end{pmatrix} \begin{pmatrix} 2 \\ 2 \end{pmatrix} \begin{pmatrix} 0 \\ 1 \end{pmatrix} \begin{pmatrix} 1 \\ 0 \end{pmatrix} \begin{pmatrix} 0 \\ -1 \end{pmatrix} \begin{pmatrix} -1 \\ 0 \end{pmatrix} \begin{pmatrix} 0 \\ 2 \end{pmatrix}$$

$$\begin{pmatrix} 2 \\ 0 \end{pmatrix} \begin{pmatrix} 0 \\ -2 \end{pmatrix} \begin{pmatrix} -2 \\ 0 \end{pmatrix} \begin{pmatrix} 0 \\ 3 \end{pmatrix} \begin{pmatrix} 3 \\ 0 \end{pmatrix} \begin{pmatrix} 0 \\ -3 \end{pmatrix} \begin{pmatrix} -3 \\ 0 \end{pmatrix} \begin{pmatrix} 1 \\ 1 \end{pmatrix}$$

$$\begin{pmatrix} 1 \\ -1 \end{pmatrix} \begin{pmatrix} -1 \\ 1 \end{pmatrix} \begin{pmatrix} -1 \\ -1 \end{pmatrix} \begin{pmatrix} 1 \\ 2 \end{pmatrix} \begin{pmatrix} 1 \\ -2 \end{pmatrix} \begin{pmatrix} -1 \\ 2 \end{pmatrix} \begin{pmatrix} -1 \\ -2 \end{pmatrix} \begin{pmatrix} 2 \\ 1 \end{pmatrix}$$

$$\begin{pmatrix} 2 \\ -1 \end{pmatrix} \begin{pmatrix} -2 \\ -2 \end{pmatrix} \begin{pmatrix} -3 \\ -3 \end{pmatrix} \begin{pmatrix} -2 \\ 1 \end{pmatrix} \begin{pmatrix} -2 \\ -1 \end{pmatrix} \begin{pmatrix} 1 \\ 3 \end{pmatrix} \begin{pmatrix} 1 \\ -3 \end{pmatrix} \begin{pmatrix} -1 \\ 3 \end{pmatrix}$$

$$\begin{pmatrix} -1 \\ -3 \end{pmatrix} \begin{pmatrix} 3 \\ 1 \end{pmatrix} \begin{pmatrix} 3 \\ -1 \end{pmatrix} \begin{pmatrix} -3 \\ 1 \end{pmatrix} \begin{pmatrix} -3 \\ -1 \end{pmatrix} \begin{pmatrix} 2 \\ 3 \end{pmatrix} \begin{pmatrix} 2 \\ -3 \end{pmatrix} \begin{pmatrix} -2 \\ 3 \end{pmatrix}$$

$$\begin{pmatrix} -2 \\ -3 \end{pmatrix} \begin{pmatrix} 3 \\ 2 \end{pmatrix} \begin{pmatrix} 3 \\ -2 \end{pmatrix} \begin{pmatrix} -3 \\ 2 \end{pmatrix} \begin{pmatrix} -3 \\ -2 \end{pmatrix} \begin{pmatrix} 3 \\ 3 \end{pmatrix} \begin{pmatrix} 3 \\ -3 \end{pmatrix} \begin{pmatrix} -3 \\ 3 \end{pmatrix}$$

REFERENCES

Thanks to B. Cherowbrier for some of the variations.

Three-D Shape Connect-Three

NAT 4
2 3 4

EQUIPMENT

Two spinners – one numbered 0 1 2 3 4, the other numbered 1 2 3 2 4
Counters of different colours
Worksheet 15 (the board) (page 92)

INSTRUCTIONS

Use the worksheet.

Trellis

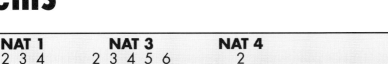

NAT 1   **NAT 3**   **NAT 4**
2 3 4   2 3 4 5 6   2

EQUIPMENT

Headless matches / cocktail sticks / anything of uniform length
Square and isometric paper
Pencil
Glue (*possibly*) for the box trellis
Trellis sheet (page 70)

INSTRUCTIONS

'Gordon got a job at the Garden Centre but he proved to be a disaster. He dropped weedkiller, tripped over bags of compost, spilled the grass seed and ran over a customer with a trolley full of potted plants. Finally the boss sent him off into the corner to get him out of the way.

In the corner were some strips of wood (all the same length) and some special fasteners to join the ends together. The boss told him to sit there and make some trellis. "We've got an order for some square trellis, use up all those strips." Gordon counted them. There were 60 strips.

What sizes/shape of trellis could he make?

Which would be the best for growing plants/which looks the neatest? etc. (He must complete every square, he must not leave a strip unconnected).

The following day they gave him 60 strips to make into triangular trellis – what sizes/shapes can he make now?'

VARIATIONS

1. 'An order comes in for box trellis to grow really fragile plants. How much box trellis will he be able to make with 60 strips?
2. They are running short of fasteners. Which designs use the least?
3. One customer always orders square trellis and always has a square shape. If he orders 1×1 you will need 4 strips and 4 fasteners, for 2×2 you'll need 12 strips and 9 fasteners. Can you work out what you'd need for a 3×3, 10×10, any size?
4. Do the same thing for equilateral triangles in triangular trellis.
5. Do the same thing for cubes in box trellis.
6. Which of these trellis patterns are rigid?
7. Make up some different shaped trellis.'

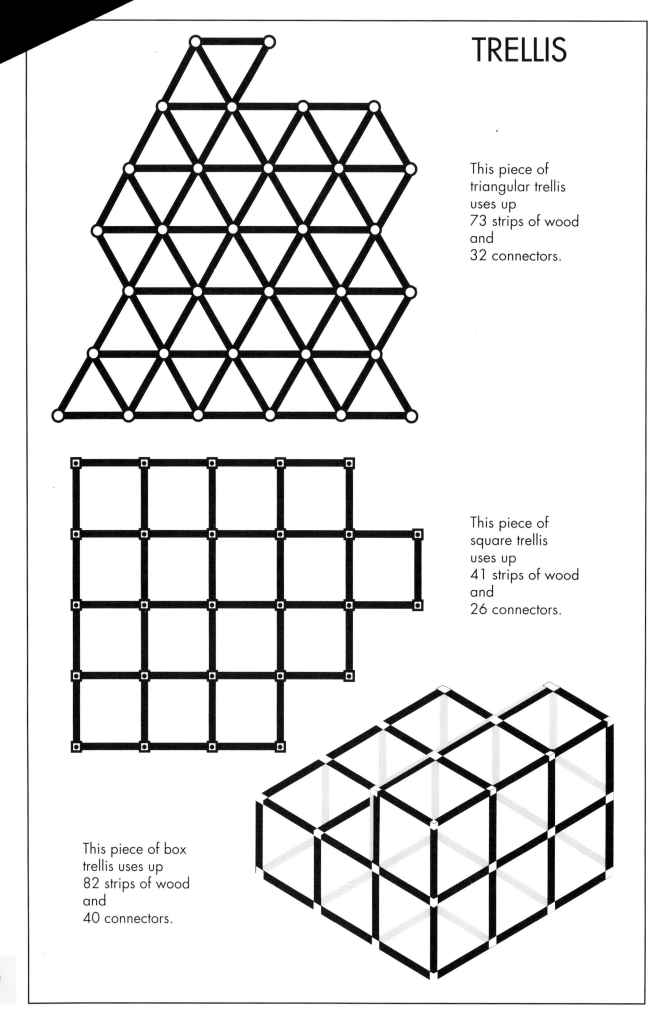

TRELLIS

This piece of triangular trellis uses up
73 strips of wood
and
32 connectors.

This piece of square trellis uses up
41 strips of wood
and
26 connectors.

This piece of box trellis uses up
82 strips of wood
and
40 connectors.

Triangles and Matches

EQUIPMENT

Paper
Pencil
Headless matches / cocktail sticks /
  anything of uniform length
Compasses (*variation 2*)

INSTRUCTIONS

1. 'You are not allowed to bend or break the matches.
2. The matches must touch ends, no overlapping or gaps.

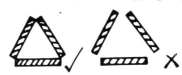

3. Find out how many different-shaped triangles you can make with various numbers of matches. Are there any numbers of matches which won't form triangles?
4. Categorize the triangles into equilateral, isosceles and scalene. For example with 9 matches you can make an equilateral (333) an isosceles (441) and a scalene (234) triangle.
5. Chart the results and look for patterns.'

VARIATIONS

1. Try to make other shapes: kites, trapezia etc.
2. Instead of using apparatus, show the class how to construct a triangle using compasses and then ask them to make triangles of various perimeters, keeping the side lengths to whole numbers.

Triangles in Triangles

EQUIPMENT

Paper
Pencil
Coloured pencils for recording

INSTRUCTIONS

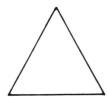  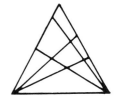

'A basic triangle with no inside lines makes one triangle.
    A triangle with a line from each bottom corner makes eight triangles.
    A triangle with two lines from each bottom corner makes how many triangles?'

VARIATIONS

1. 'Start with only one line from one corner, two lines from one corner etc.
2. Try one line from the left corner but two from the right etc.
3. Try one line from *each* corner, two from each corner etc.'

71

wo Dice

NAT 1	NAT 5
2 3 4 5	3 4 5 6 7

EQUIPMENT

Paper
Pencil
Dice

INSTRUCTIONS

A game for 4 players.
'Each player chooses one of the following sets of numbers.

6	7		10	2	12	11		4	9	3		8	5

Take turns to throw two dice.
Every time the numbers on the dice add to one of the numbers in your set, score one point.
Throw the dice fifty times.
Which set of numbers did you expect to win?
What did happen? Why?'

REFERENCES

Starter idea from the periodical 'Struggle' vol. 2 produced and published by Maths Association and National Association for Remedial Education.

VARIATIONS

1. 'Make up different sets of numbers and test them.
2. Can you make a set which would give all players an equal chance of winning?
3. Vary the number of players.
4. What about sets for using with three dice, four dice etc.
5. Use 8- or 10- or 12-sided dice.'

Vector Games

NAT 1	NAT 4
2 3 4	8

EQUIPMENT

Dice of different colours
Counters of different colours
Pack of vector cards (Game 3)
Worksheets 16–19 (the board) (pages 93–96)
Plus/minus paper onto which the dice are thrown (see Worksheet 17)

INSTRUCTIONS

The vector games which follow have the instructions written on. The third board (Tunnel Vision) is for the pupils to make up their own game, after having tried out some of the others.

VARIATIONS

VECTOR GAME 1 ALTERNATIVES

1. Instead of two different dice players could play with two the same and decide the order which would be most advantageous after each throw.
2. It *does* matter if a player overshoots, if a throw would take their counter over the edge they miss that turn.
3. If a player reaches a side they have already touched they don't start again at the centre, but wait until they throw a vector which will take them back on to the board.
4. If a player lands on an opponent's counter, the opponent has to go back to the centre.
5. Corners count as *both* the sides meeting there.

6. Write the positive and negative number on the axes and players have to state the co-ordinates of their destination before being allowed to land there.

7. Colour each side differently and give each player four counters, one of each colour. Each player sticks his or her initials (sticky paper) on the counters. When a player gets a counter to the side with the matching colour it stays there and next turn he or she throws and starts the most appropriate colour counter off from the centre. For example for a throw of $\begin{pmatrix} 1 \\ -6 \end{pmatrix}$, if the bottom edge were blue, the player would start the blue counter.

8. Number the edges from 0 on the axis, to 10 in the corner. You still try for 4 edges, but the nearer the corner you land, the higher the score. Corners count as *one* side and you must state

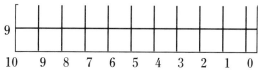

which. If you land on the axis line you needn't count that score but try again from the centre. The players don't cross out the sides as they reach them but write their score next to each one. The score of your *first* landing on that side is the only one to count if you land on a side more than once. The first to touch all sides gets 2 bonus points and then the scores are added to decide the winner.

Most of these alternative rules make the game more complicated, so it is best to start with the basic ones. Pupils will probably also suggest changes of their own. The L, S and E circles can, of course, be put anywhere, increased, decreased or left out altogether.

VECTOR GAME 2 – VECTOR MESSAGES:
Write letters and punctuation marks on most of the intersections of a large grid. Start from the centre of the grid and make up a message: write down the vectors that you need to move in order to spell out the words of the message.

Give it to someone else to decode. They must move as shown by the vectors to spell out the message.

VECTOR GAME 3 – VECTOR AIMING HIGH
A game for 2–4 players. Write addition, subtraction or multiplication operators (e.g. $+2$, -7, $\times 4$) on every intersection of a large grid. Leave a space in the centre to put S for start. Each player is dealt 10 cards (made up as for Target, page 68) and has a starting score of 10. Each player in turn plays a vector card, moves his counter according to the vector shown and then works out his score according to the operator he lands on. When everyone has had 20 moves the game ends. The winner is the player with the highest score. If any vector takes a player off the board, he must go back to S.

How can each game be improved?
Do the rules work?
Is it fair/does each game last long enough/too long?

The Wall

EQUIPMENT

Pencil
Paper
Wall sheets (page 75) or small squared paper
Calculator (*optional*)

INSTRUCTIONS

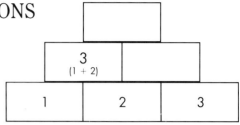

1. 'Draw a wall with a 3-brick base.
2. Fill in the digits 1, 2, 3 in the bottom layer.
3. Add the 2 bricks below to get the answer for the brick above (as shown).
4. What is the number in the top brick?

Use 1, 2 and 3 again but in a different order.
Do you get the same answer in the top brick?
How many different answers are possible in the top brick?
Which is the largest?
Which is the smallest?'

VARIATIONS

1. 'Try 4/5/6 base walls.
2. Try multiplying instead of adding (you may need a calculator).
3. What happens with decimals/fractions?
4. What happens if you subtract instead of add?
5. Can you work backwards from the top number to find the base numbers?'

Weighing Activities

EQUIPMENT

11 Activity cards
Peppercorns, wheat, cat biscuits, large box of matches, rice, feathers
Various metric weights
Jewellers', or scientific scales
Various weighing machines, balances
Labels showing both the imperial and the metric weight
Spring balance calibrated in newtons

INSTRUCTIONS

Organization of this depends on the class. Usually pupils will work in pairs on an activity but will write up individually what they found.

Alternatively a small group or an individual can be given a card to do when everyone else is busy.

Example:

WEIGHING ACTIVITY CARD

The Problem:

> Weigh the box of matches. How much do you think the <u>box</u> weighs? How much do you think each match weighs? Can you find out how much each match weighs? How much would 1000 matches weigh? How many matches would you get in 400g?

Write out the problem in your own words. You may want to draw the equipment you are using. Describe each stage of your work so that someone else can understand what you did.

PROBLEMS

How much does an average peppercorn weigh? How much would 100 of them weigh? How many peppercorns would there be in half a pound? Or in 250 g?

You have three 50 g weights and four 20 g weights. What amounts are you able to weigh out? Can some be done in more than one way? What if you are using a balance instead of scales? Try a different set of weights.

How much does an average grain of wheat weigh? How much would 100 grains weigh? How many grains would you get in a Kg? In a half-hundredweight?

How much does an average cat biscuit weigh? How much would 10 biscuits weigh? How many biscuits would there be in a 300 g box?

Weigh the box of matches. Can you find out how much each match weighs? How much would 1000 weigh? How many matches would you get in 400 g?

Do all the weighing machines agree. Make up a way of testing them. If they don't agree is there any way to alter them?

Here are some labels showing weights in imperial and metric. Can you use them to make up a conversion table showing grams and Kilograms changed into ounces and pounds?

What is a newton? How many newtons does a pound weight produce? Or a Kilogram weight? Or 2 lbs? or 500 g?

Which is heavier, a pound of rice or a pound of feathers?! How many grains of rice are there to a pound? How many feathers to a pound?

Wipers

NAT 1	NAT 3	NAT 5
2 3 4 5	2 3 4 5	2 3 4 5

EQUIPMENT

Stopwatch or timer
Co-operation of several car drivers
   (staff, parents etc.)
Hosepipe or watering can

INSTRUCTIONS

'Find out:
1. How many speeds of windscreen wiper has each car got?
2. Time them – how many wipes per minute?
3. Decide how many speeds are necessary to cope with wet conditions from cloudburst to drizzle.
4. When you've decided how many speeds, you must also decide what speeds e.g. 60 wipes per minute etc.
5. Write and ask car manufacturers why they use the speeds they do.
6. Write to the Road Research Laboratory, Crowthorne, Berkshire and ask if any results are available.
7. Question the AA and the RAC.
8. Draw graphs to show your results.'

VARIATIONS

1. Include some cars with rear-window wipers.
2. Look at the position of the windscreen-washer nozzles. Which is the best position, and the best angle. (Take into account the slant of the windscreen). The optimum angle will obviously be different for a stationary vehicle and for one travelling at 70 m.p.h.

Wreckedangles

NAT 1	NAT 3
2 3 4	2 3 4 5 6

EQUIPMENT

A sheet of rectangles or squared
   paper
Paper
Pencil
Ruler

INSTRUCTIONS

'Draw a straight line across the first rectangle.
How many regions does this give you?
Draw two straight lines across the second rectangle.
How many regions this time? Is this the most?
How many different answers are there?
Try 3 . . . 4 . . . 5 . . . lines. Draw all the different answers.
Underline the biggest and smallest answers each time.
Can you see any patterns?'

VARIATIONS

'Try it with an apple:
One straight cut with a knife gives you how many pieces?
2 straight cuts . . . 3 . . . 4 . . . etc.
You will probably need help holding all the bits together for the fourth cut!
What is the most pieces you can make with 4 cuts?
Can you work out what it would be for 5 cuts?'

Alien Bricks WORKSHEET 1

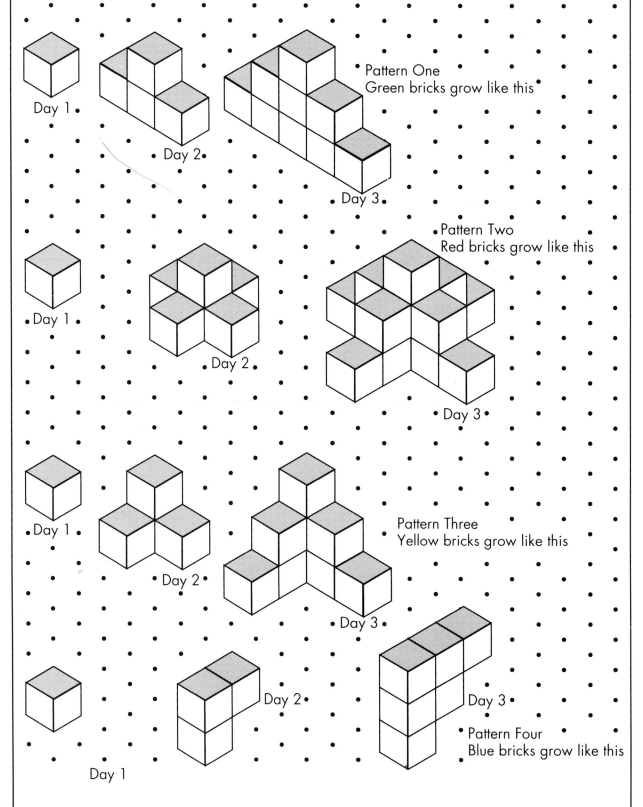

Energy Converter Growth Patterns

Day 1

Day 2

Day 3

Pattern One
Green bricks grow like this

Day 1

Day 2

Day 3

Pattern Two
Red bricks grow like this

Day 1

Day 2

Day 3

Pattern Three
Yellow bricks grow like this

Day 1

Day 2

Day 3

Pattern Four
Blue bricks grow like this

Blockbusters WORKSHEET 2

A game for 2 players.
Players choose which colour counters they are going to use.
Player 1 throws both dice. Add, subtract, multiply or divide the two
numbers to get an answer on the board. Cover it with a counter.
Player 2 has a turn. Only one counter is allowed on each number.
The first to complete a path from side to side, or top to bottom is
the winner.

Colouring Areas WORKSHEET 3

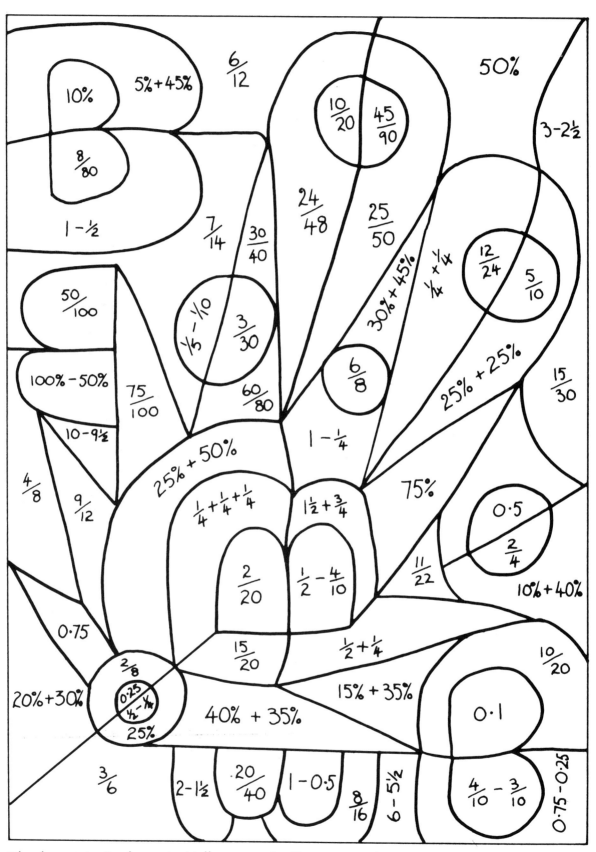

Black = ¼, Red = ½, Yellow = ¾, Green = 1/10.

Colouring Areas WORKSHEET 4

Colour all ½ and ¼ equivalents.

Colouring Areas WORKSHEET 5

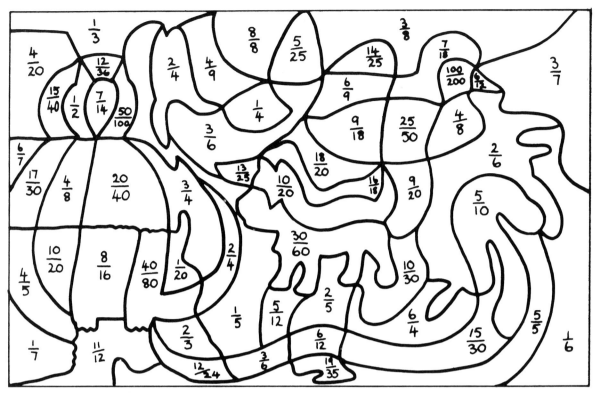

Colour in fractions equivalent to a half.

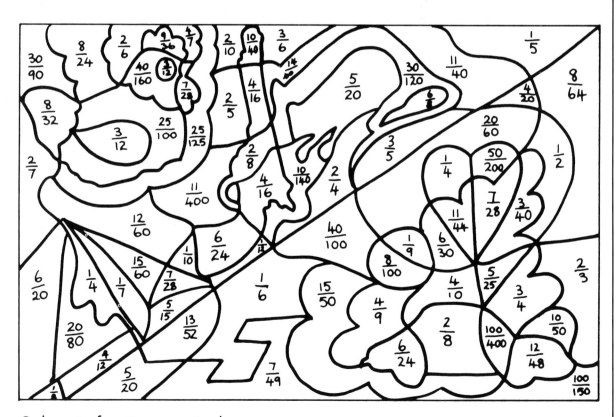

Colour in fractions equivalent to a quarter.

Fred's Bread WORKSHEET 6

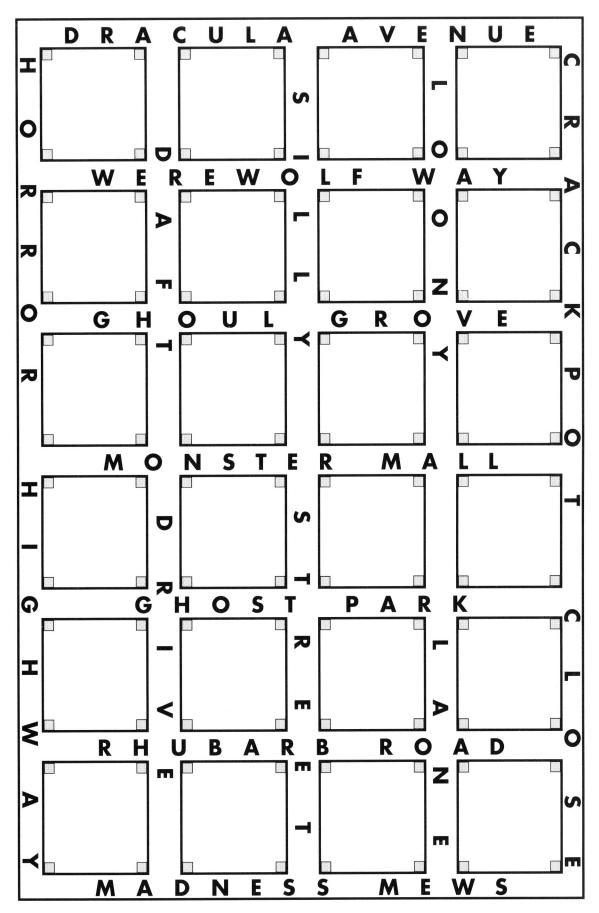

Millions WORKSHEET 7

1. What day of the week will it be in a million seconds' time?

2. What year was it a million minutes ago?

3. Have you lived a million hours yet?

4. Which century will it be in a million days' time?

5. How many hundredweight bags will you need for a million ounces of coal?

6. How many lorries, each able to carry 10 tons, would be needed to shift a million lb of rock?

7. How rich are you if you have a million pence?

8. If you travelled a million inches would you get to Bristol?

9. If you travelled a million feet would you get to Liverpool?

10. If you travelled a million yards would you get to Scotland?

11. If an author writes a million words how many average-size pages will he or she fill? How many average-size paperback books is this?

12. You have a million little tiles one inch square. Will you have enough to cover a football pitch completely?

13. You have a grassy field of 20 acres which you are going to strip of turf to sell. You cut the turf in one foot squares. Will you get a million turves from your field?

14. Cats-eyes are placed at intervals of 17 feet. If you have a million of them will you have enough to reach across America from coast to coast?

Make up some more questions of your own. Try using billions, trillions . . . or even googols (1 with 100 zeros!).

Number Wheels WORKSHEET 8

1.

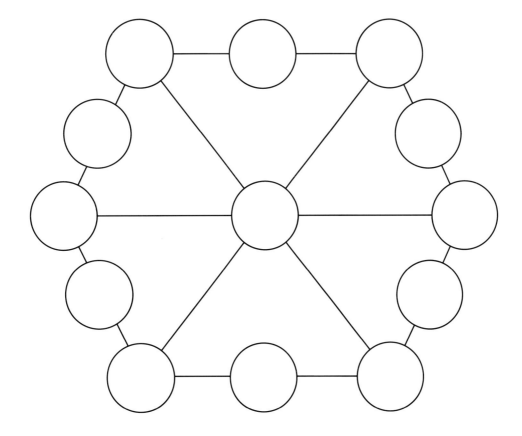

2.

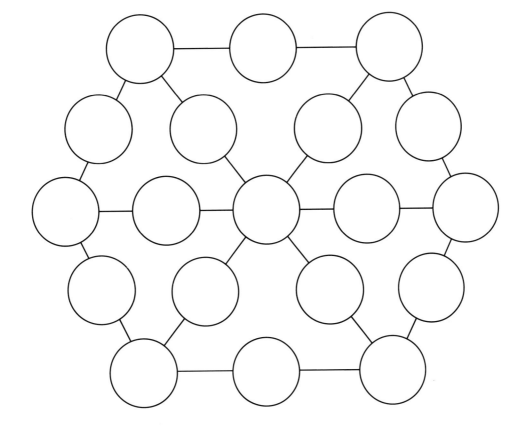

Number Wheels WORKSHEET 9

3.

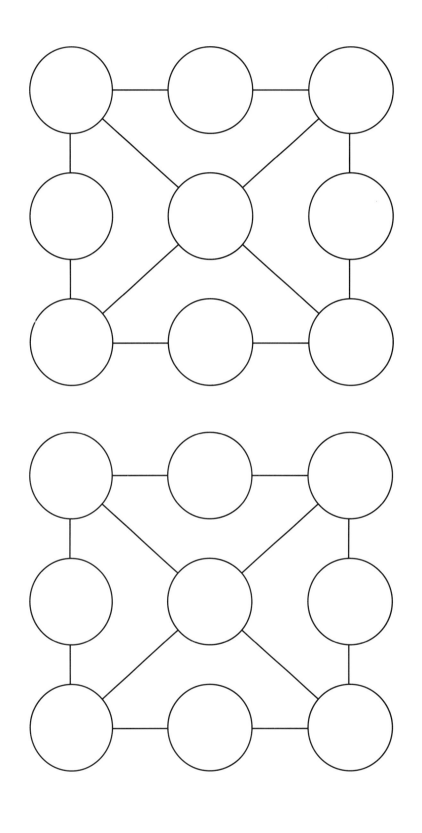

Number Wheels WORKSHEET 10

4.

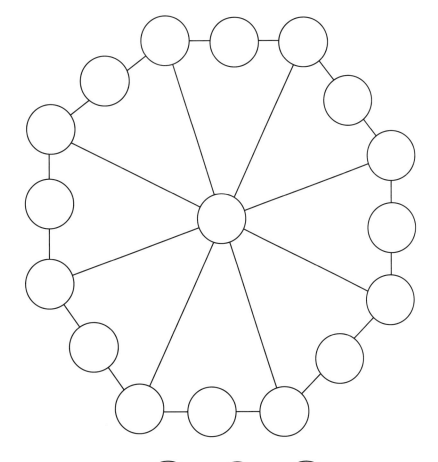

5.

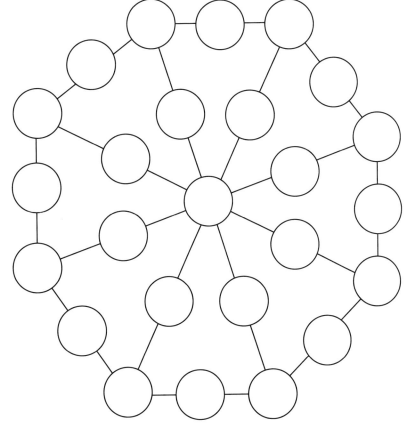

Pictures from Bearings WORKSHEET 11

Method 1 Starting at B, draw in a line of the length and bearing specified, move your protractor to the end of the line drawn (draw in faint North lines if necessary) and take your next bearing from there. See what shape these bearings will produce. Distances are in centimetres.

(080,2) (040,3) (090,6) (120,3) (100,4) (160,1) (180,1) (270,2) (210,1) (270,1) (330,1) (270,8) (210,1) (270,1) (330,1) (280,1½)

B
•

Method 2 Take *all* the bearings from the same point. Join them up in order, to reveal the shape. See what shape these bearings will produce. Distances are in centimetres.

(360,4) (020,4) (025,5) (035,3½) (060,2½) (070,4) (070,2½) (080,4) (080,2½) (090,4) (090,2½) (120,1½) (130,1½) (180,1½) (230,1½) (240,1½) 270,2½) (270,4) (280,2½) (280,4) (290,2½) (290,4) (300,2½) (325,3½) (335,5) (340,4) (360,4)

•

Probability Mazes WORKSHEET 12

Maze One

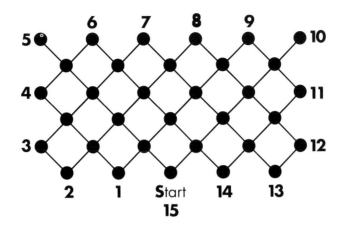

Rules

Throw one die. If it shows 1 or 2, go left. If it shows 3 or 4, go right. If it shows 5 or 6, go straight. (If you throw 5 or 6 on the first go, throw again).

When you reach one of the 15 exits, stop and record it.

If you threw 1, 3, 4, 6, you would emerge from exit 14.

If you threw 2, 5, 5, 6, 3, you would emerge from exit 6. (Right/left/straight on are in relationship to the path just travelled, *not* to the start of the maze).

Maze Two

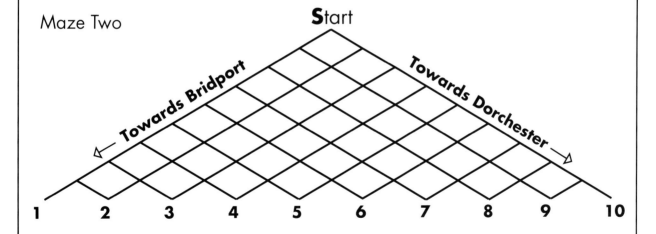

Rules

Throw one die. If it shows an even number, move towards Bridport. If it shows an odd number, move towards Dorchester. Record where you finish.

If you threw 1, 2, 2, 6, 4, 1, 5, 5, 3, you would finish at point 6.

If you threw 2, 6, 3, 4, 6, 5, 2, 1, 6, you would finish at point 4.

Maze Three

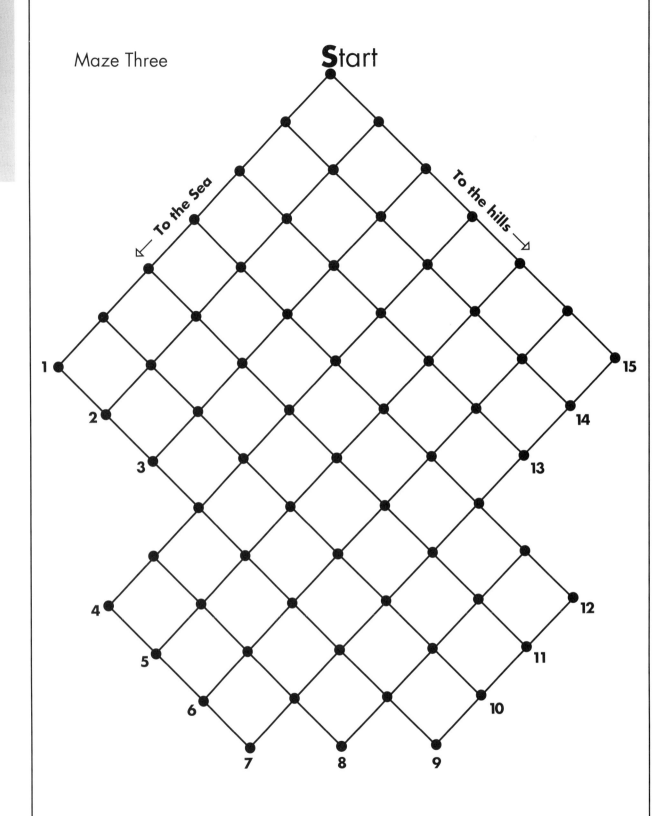

Start

To the Sea

To the hills

Rules
Throw two dice and add up the scores. If you score over 8, move towards the sea. If you score 8 or under, move towards the hills. Which exits are the most/least likely? How many people, out of 50 who start, will be able to go for a swim?

Sheep Dealer WORKSHEET 14

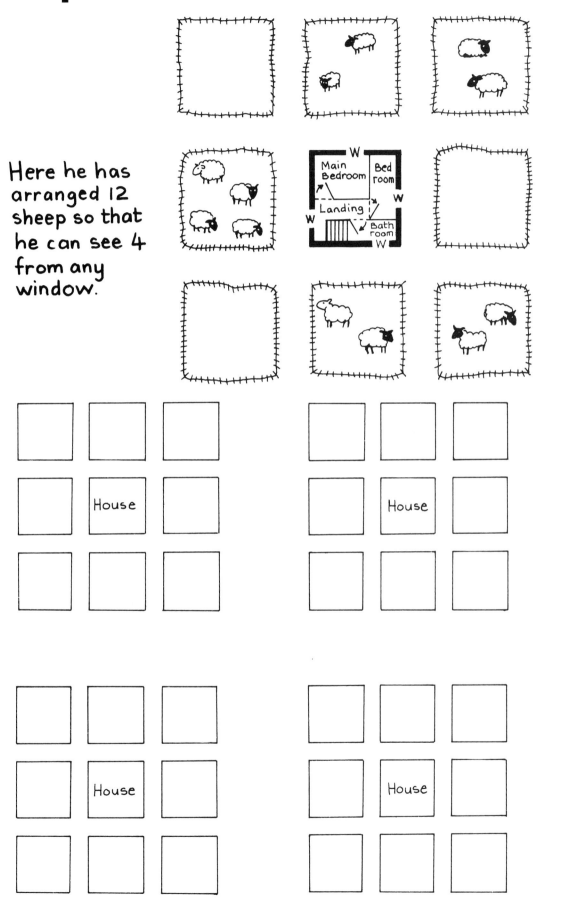

Here he has arranged 12 sheep so that he can see 4 from any window.

Three-D Shape Connect-Three

WORKSHEET 15

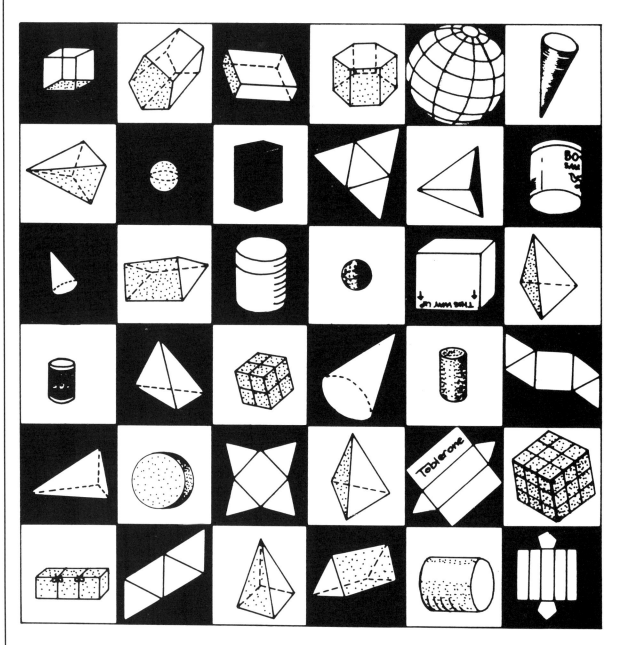

A game for 2 players.
1. Players choose which colour counters they are going to use.
2. Player 1 spins both spinners and adds their results together. Look on the board for a solid with that number of faces. If you find one and name it correctly, you can put one of your colour counters on that square. If you can't find one, or you give it the wrong name, you lose your go.
3. Now it's Player 2's turn. The winner is the first player to get three of their counters in a row, vertically, horizontally *or* diagonally.

Vector Game 1 WORKSHEET 16

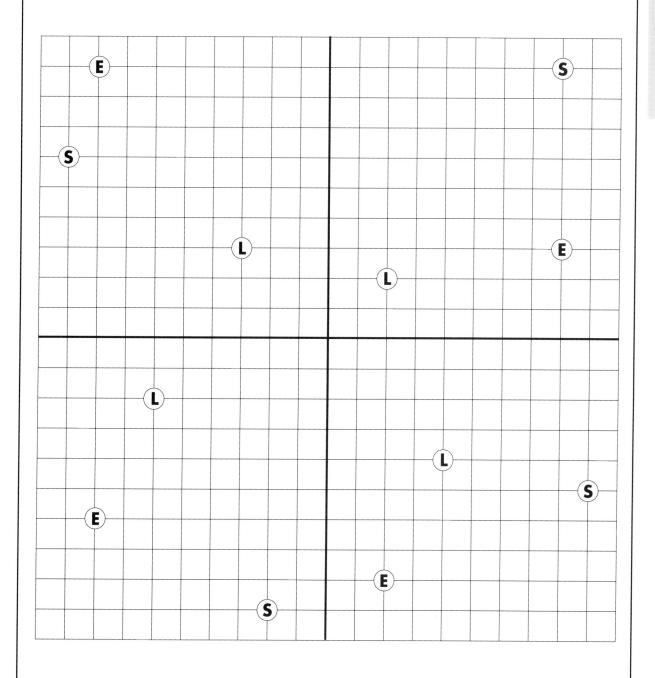

Vector Game 1 WORKSHEET 17

A game for 2–4 players.

1. First decide which die means which direction e.g. red die = up/down, blue die 5 left/right.

2. Player 1 places his or her counter on the centre starting point. He or she then rolls or drops the dice on to the plus/minus paper and moves the counter accordingly.

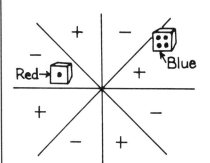

For example this throw would produce a movement of 4 to the right and 1 down, i.e. a vector of $\begin{pmatrix} +4 \\ -1 \end{pmatrix}$

If a die lands exactly half way across a line or there is argument about which side it should be, it must be thrown again.

3. Then Player 2 starts the same way.

4. The aim is to touch all four sides of the board. When you have reached a side you start again (when it's your turn again) at the centre. Each player might have a piece of paper with 'Top, Bottom, Left and Right' on it, and cross off the sides as he or she touches them. If you reach the same side twice it only counts once. Corners count as *one* of the two sides which meet there. A player reaching a corner must state which side they are crossing off.

5. If your counter lands on an opponent's counter it doesn't matter. If you thrown *more* than you need to get *to* the edge, then you just move your counter to the edge. If you throw more in both directions then the left/right movement must be done first.

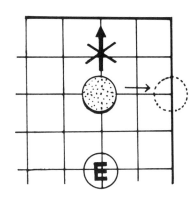

In this example a throw of $\begin{pmatrix} +4 \\ -3 \end{pmatrix}$ would get to the top or the right sides but the *across* movement must be done first, so your counter moves to the right hand edge only.

6. If you land on an E you can cross off an extra side – but you must say which one you are crossing off.

If you land on an L you lose a go.

If you land on an S you must move back to the centre start position.

Vector Snakes & Ladders

WORKSHEET 18

A game for 2–6 players.
Play this game in the same way as snakes and ladders. The vectors are both snakes *and* ladders.

First to reach the 'Finish' square *exactly* is the winner. (If you throw too many, you move up and then back).

Finish	98	$\binom{2}{-4}_{97}$	96	95	$\binom{2}{-1}_{94}$	93	92	91	$\binom{-2}{0}_{90}$
80	$\binom{3}{-1}_{81}$	82	83	84	85	$\binom{-2}{-1}_{86}$	87	$\binom{1}{-6}_{88}$	89
79	78	$\binom{3}{1}_{77}$	$\binom{0}{-2}_{76}$	75	74	73	$\binom{1}{-1}_{72}$	71	70
$\binom{2}{-1}_{60}$	61	62	63	$\binom{-1}{2}_{64}$	65	66	67	68	$\binom{0}{-2}_{69}$
59	$\binom{2}{2}_{58}$	57	56	55	54	$\binom{-6}{-1}_{53}$	52	51	50
40	41	42	$\binom{1}{3}_{43}$	44	$\binom{3}{-1}_{45}$	46	47	$\binom{-1}{-2}_{48}$	49
39	$\binom{-1}{-1}_{38}$	$\binom{-2}{1}_{37}$	36	35	34	33	$\binom{-4}{-1}_{32}$	31	$\binom{0}{2}_{30}$
20	$\binom{-1}{-2}_{21}$	22	23	24	$\binom{1}{5}_{25}$	26	27	28	29
$\binom{0}{3}_{19}$	18	17	$\binom{1}{2}_{16}$	15	14	13	$\binom{5}{-1}_{12}$	11	10
start	1	2	$\binom{-1}{2}_{3}$	4	5	$\binom{2}{2}_{6}$	7	$\binom{-4}{1}_{8}$	9

Vector Tunnel Vision WORKSHEET 19

G GUARDPOST

T TUNNEL

B BUNKHOUSE